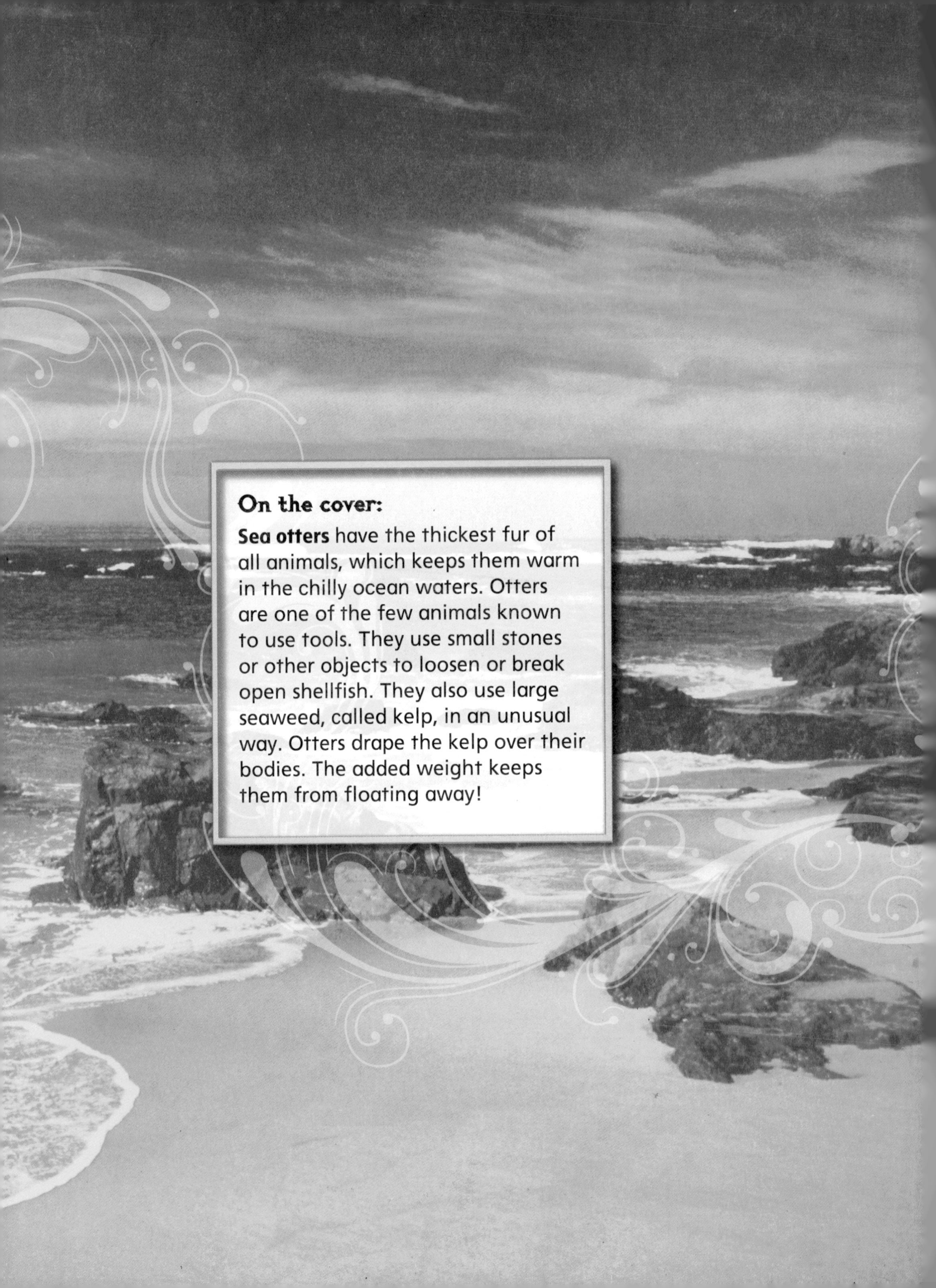

On the cover:

Sea otters have the thickest fur of all animals, which keeps them warm in the chilly ocean waters. Otters are one of the few animals known to use tools. They use small stones or other objects to loosen or break open shellfish. They also use large seaweed, called kelp, in an unusual way. Otters drape the kelp over their bodies. The added weight keeps them from floating away!

A Reading/Language Arts Program

Program Authors

Diane August
Donald R. Bear
Janice A. Dole
Jana Echevarria
Douglas Fisher
David Francis
Vicki Gibson
Jan E. Hasbrouck
Scott G. Paris
Timothy Shanahan
Josefina V. Tinajero

Mc Graw Hill Macmillan/McGraw-Hill

Contributors

Time Magazine, Accelerated Reader

RFB&D

learning through listening

Students with print disabilities may be eligible to obtain an accessible, audio version of the pupil edition of this textbook. Please call Recording for the Blind & Dyslexic at 1-800-221-4792 for complete information.

B

The McGraw·Hill Companies

Macmillan/McGraw-Hill

Published by Macmillan/McGraw-Hill, of McGraw-Hill Education, a division of The McGraw-Hill Companies, Inc., Two Penn Plaza, New York, New York 10121.

Printed in the United States of America

ISBN: 978-0-02-199963-7/1, Bk. 3

MHID: 0-02-199963-5/1, Bk. 3

6 7 8 9 (RJE/LEH) 12 11

Welcome to
California *Treasures*

Imagine having a pet dinosaur who wants to go to school, learning about how *real* animals act as teams, or reading about a kitten who thinks the moon is a bowl of milk. Your **Student Book** contains these and other award-winning fiction and nonfiction selections.

Treasures Meets California Standards

The instruction provided with each reading selection in your **Student Book** will ensure that you meet all the **California Reading/Language Arts Standards** for your grade. Throughout the book, special symbols (such as ✔) and codes (such as R 1.1.2) have been added to show where and how these standards are being met. They will help you know *what* you are learning and *why*.

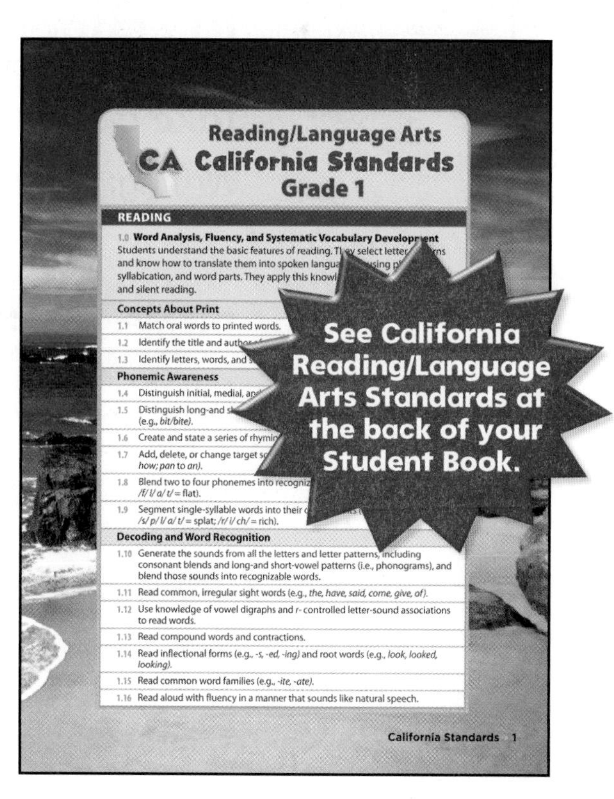

Reading/Language Arts
CA California Standards
Grade 1

READING

1.0 **Word Analysis, Fluency, and Systematic Vocabulary Development**
Students understand the basic features of reading. They select letter patterns and know how to translate them into spoken langua... using p... syllabication, and word parts. They apply this knowl... and silent reading.

Concepts About Print

1.1 Match oral words to printed words.
1.2 Identify the title and author...
1.3 Identify letters, words, and s...

Phonemic Awareness

1.4 Distinguish initial, medial, an...
1.5 Distinguish long-and sh... (e.g., *bit/bite*).
1.6 Create and state a series of rhymin...
1.7 Add, delete, or change target so... *how; pan* to *an*).
1.8 Blend two to four phonemes into recogniz... /f/ l/ a/ t/ = flat).
1.9 Segment single-syllable words into their c... /s/ p/ l/ a/ t/ = splat; /r/ i/ ch/ = rich).

Decoding and Word Recognition

1.10 Generate the sounds from all the letters and letter patterns, including consonant blends and long-and short-vowel patterns (i.e., phonograms), and blend those sounds into recognizable words.
1.11 Read common, irregular sight words (e.g., *the, have, said, come, give, of*).
1.12 Use knowledge of vowel digraphs and *r*- controlled letter-sound associations to read words.
1.13 Read compound words and contractions.
1.14 Read inflectional forms (e.g., *-s, -ed, -ing*) and root words (e.g., *look, looked, looking*).
1.15 Read common word families (e.g., *-ite, -ate*).
1.16 Read aloud with fluency in a manner that sounds like natural speech.

California Standards 1

See California
Reading/Language
Arts Standards at
the back of your
Student Book.

What do these symbols mean?

 = Tested Standards in California

 = Skill or Strategy that will appear on your test

R = Reading Standards

W = Writing Standards

LC = Language Conventions Standards

LAS = Listening and Speaking Standards

Macmillan/McGraw-Hill

Creative Expression

Have Fun!

THE BIG QUESTION

THEME: Let's Laugh

THEME: Family Fun

THEME: Making Art

THEME: Being Creative

THEME: Kids Around the World

STANDARDS PRACTICE: Show What you Know

Unit 3
Have Fun

The Big Question

How can we have fun?

Theme Launcher Video

LOG ON Find out more about how kids have fun at www.macmillanmh.com.

READ TOGETHER

The
Big
Question
How can we have fun?

If you could do anything you wanted, what would you do? Would you make something out of paper or blocks? Would you read a book? Would you kick a ball with your friends? Or would you just sit under a tree and daydream?

There are lots of ways to have fun. What makes you and your friends laugh? Do you think children in other lands would laugh at the same things? How do you have fun?

Research Activities

Make a joke and riddle book. Ask family or friends to share their favorite jokes. Write one down. Draw a picture to go with it. Put all your jokes and riddles together into a class book.

Keep Track of Ideas

As you read, keep track of different kinds of fun on the Three-Tab organizer. Use categories such as Games, Making Things, or Being Silly. Draw and write about each kind of fun.

Research Toolkit

Conduct Your Unit 3 Research Online with:

Research Roadmap
Follow step-by-step guide to complete your research project.

Online Resources
- Topic Finder and other Research Tools
- Videos and Virtual Fieldtrips
- Photos and Drawings for Presentations
- Related Articles and Web Resources

California Web Site Links

Go to **www.macmillanmh.com** for more information.

California People

David Diaz
Children's Book Illustrator
David Diaz illustrates children's books and also does ceramic art. He started drawing in the first grade.

CA Talk About It
What makes you laugh? How do you make other people laugh?
LOG ON
Find out more about things that make you laugh at www.macmillanmh.com.
Let's Laugh

Jane Is Late!

Words to Know

why
school
today
away
way

Why is Jane late for **school today**?
She wants to see some frogs at play.

The frogs hop up and hop **away**.
They make Jane very late today!

Why is Jane late on her **way** back?
She wants to see the ducks that quack.

The ducks are glad to see her, too.
They are quacking, "We like you!"

Comprehension

Genre
In a **Rhyming Story**, some words end with the same sounds.

Visualize

Retell
Use your Retelling Chart.

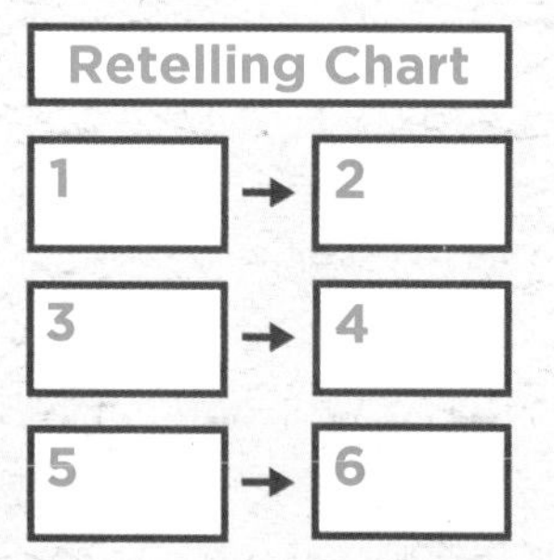

Read to Find Out

What happens to the boy on his way to school?

On My Way to School

by Wong Herbert Yee

On my **way** to **school today**,
a pig asks me to come and play.

It's not just a pig.
It's a pig in a wig!
We run for the bus,
just the two of us.

Pig and I run fast, fast, fast!
We get on the bus at last.
Huff, puff! The bus zips **away**.
Pig makes me late for school today!

On my way to school, we pass
a trash truck that ran out of gas.
On top of that truck,
sit two apes and a duck!

Apes and a duck hop in the bus.
They sit down with the rest of us.

Slip, flip! The bus zips away.
Apes make me late for school today!

On my way to school, I see
frogs up in a gumdrop tree.

Plip, plop! The gumdrops drop.
Two frogs cut. Two frogs mop.

Frogs hop in the bus.
They sit down with the rest of us.
Hip! Hop! The bus zips away.
Frogs make me late for school today!

Here we go, just one last stop.
Frogs hop in the lake. Plip, plop!

Duck is off to get some gas.
Apes fish and nap in the grass.

Tick, tock! The bus zips away.
It looks like I am late today!

Now the bus drops me off at school.
I see a crocodile slink out of a pool!

I think it slid under the gate.
And that, Miss Blake, is **why** I am late!

READ TOGETHER

On the Way with Wong Herbert Yee

Wong Herbert Yee says, "No bus picked me up at the corner. I walked a mile to get to school! When I write, I use things that really happened. My imagination fills in the rest. Remember what you see, read, and hear. You may write a funny story, too!"

Other books
by Wong Herbert Yee

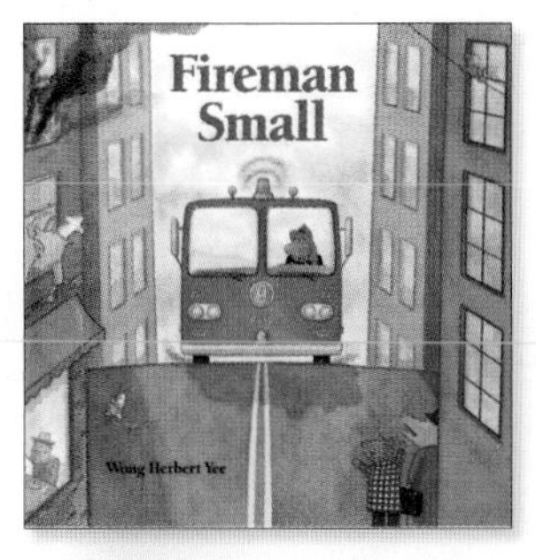

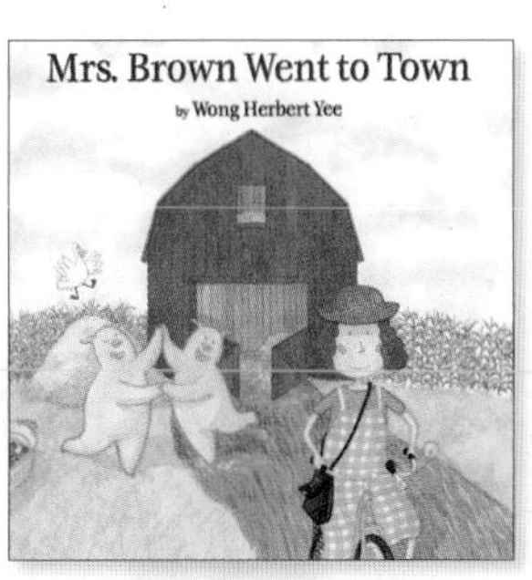

LOG ON Find out more about Wong Herbert Yee at **www.macmillanmh.com**.

CA Author's Purpose

Wong Herbert Yee wanted to write a funny story about getting to school. Draw how you get to school. Write about it.

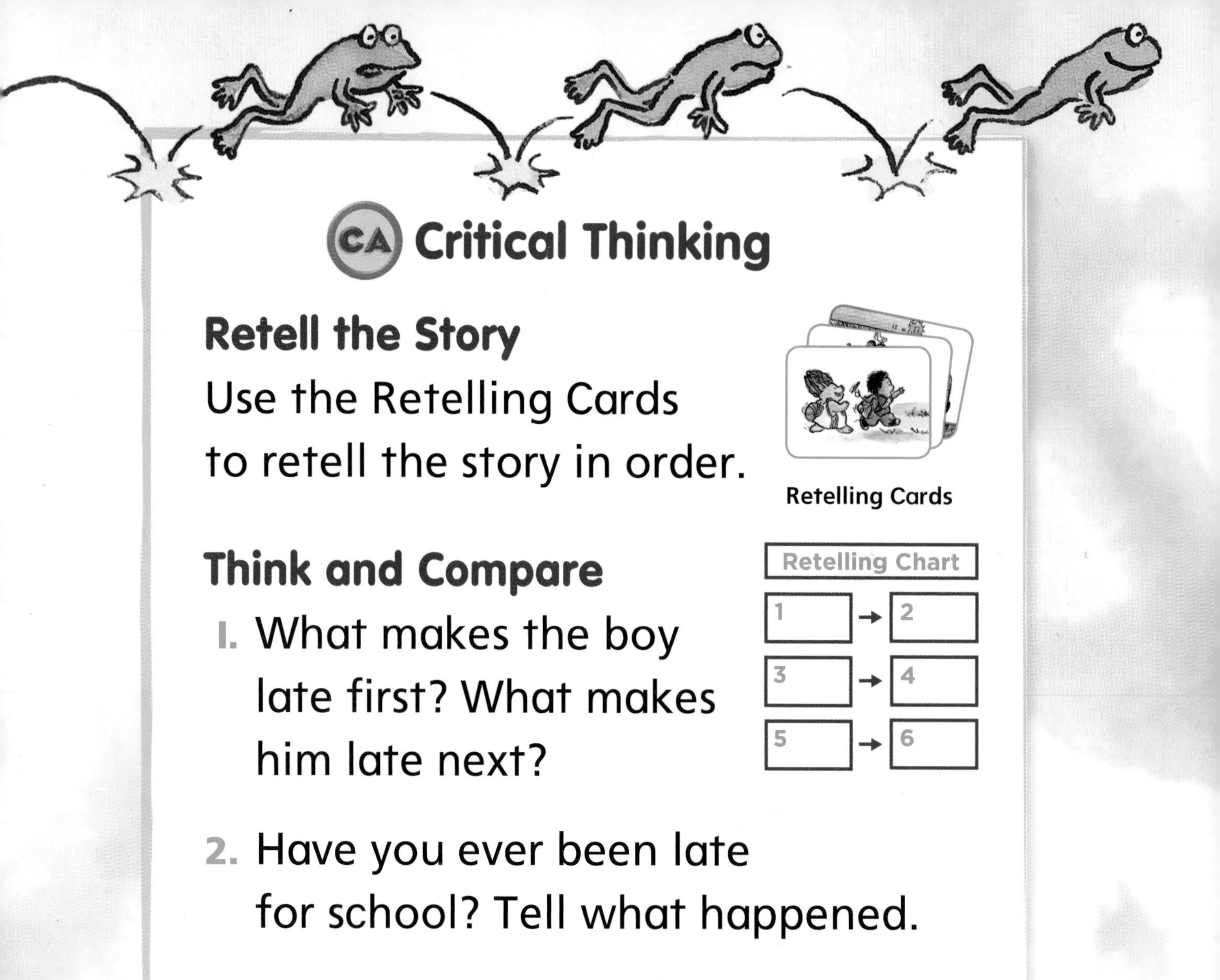

Critical Thinking

Retell the Story

Use the Retelling Cards
to retell the story in order.

Retelling Cards

Think and Compare

1. What makes the boy late first? What makes him late next?
2. Have you ever been late for school? Tell what happened.
3. Could this story really happen? Tell why or why not.
4. How are *On My Way to School* and "Jane is Late!" the same?

Language Arts

Genre
Humor A riddle is a question with a clever, funny answer.

Text Feature
A Sign uses words or pictures to give information.

LOG ON Find out more about riddles at www.macmillanmh.com.

READ TOGETHER

Take a Riddle Ride

Get Ready to Laugh!

What do you say to a runaway traffic sign?

Stop, sign!

Why did the dog cross
the road?

To get to the barking lot.

What's yellow outside, gray inside, and very crowded?

A school bus full of elephants.

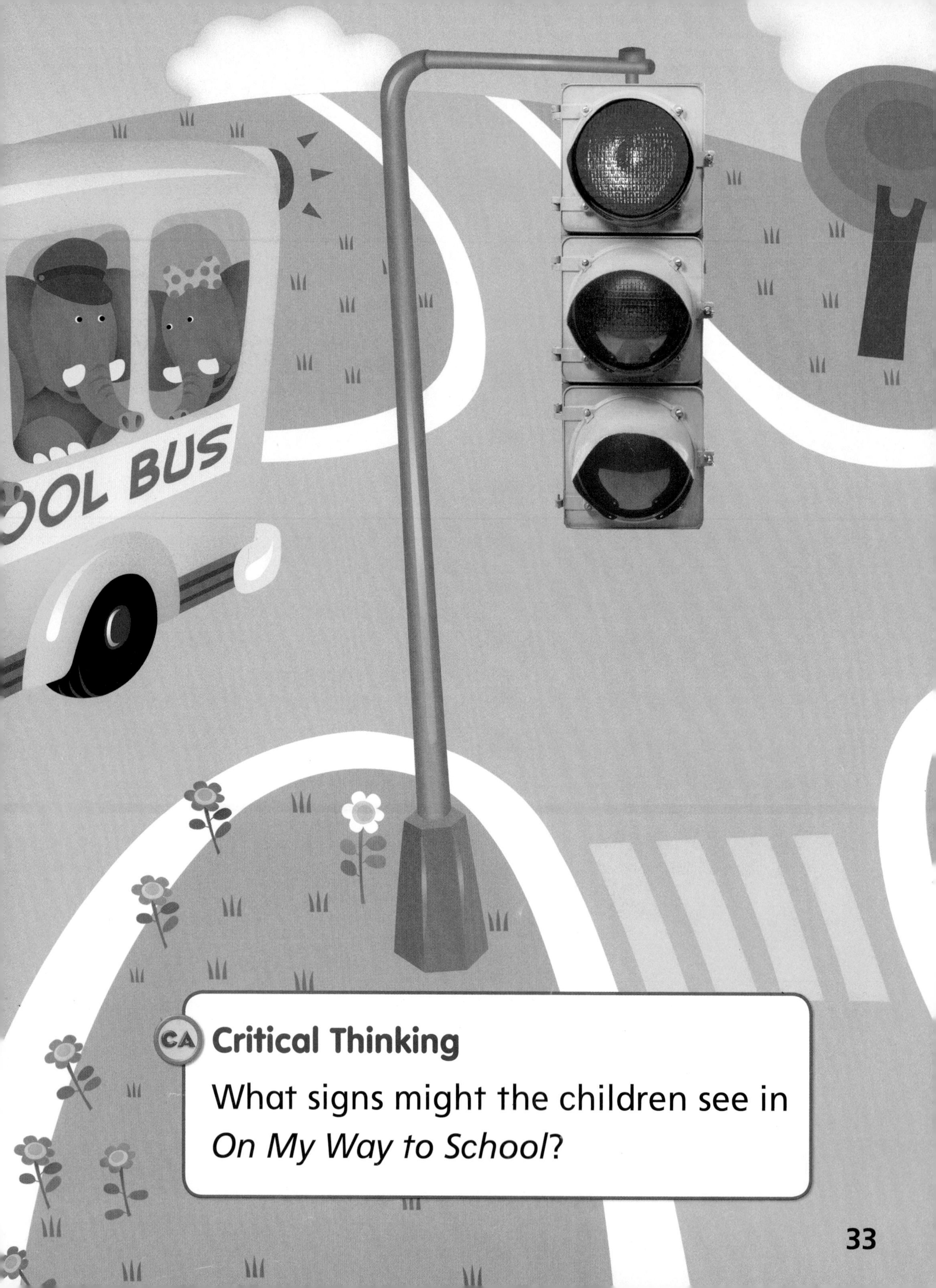

Critical Thinking

What signs might the children see in *On My Way to School*?

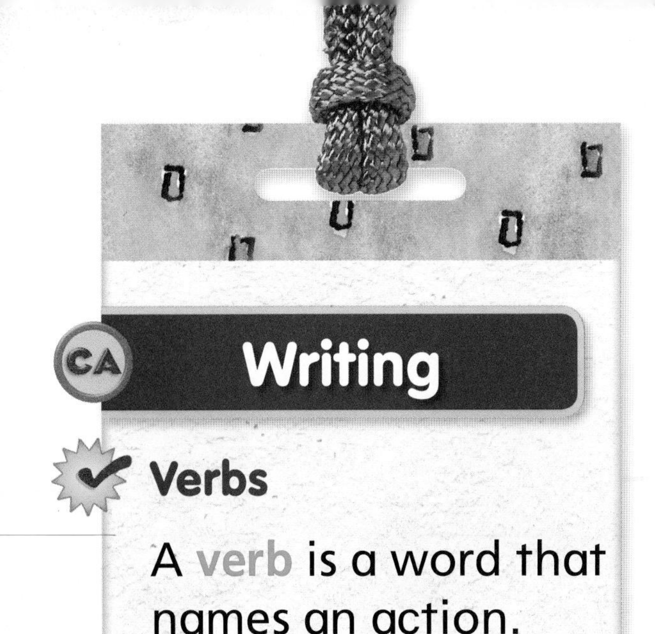

CA **Writing**

Verbs

A **verb** is a word that names an action.

Write a Silly Rhyme

Callie wrote a silly rhyme about a cat.

Dogs
Most cats like to jump and run.
My cat likes to read for fun.

Your Turn

Imagine something silly.

Write a rhyme about it.

Use an action word.

Writer's Checklist

- ☐ Did I write about something silly?
- ☐ Do some words rhyme?
- ☐ Does my rhyme have an action word?

Family Fun

CA
Talk About It
What do you like to do with your family? How do you have fun together?
LOG ON
Find out more about family fun at www.macmillanmh.com.

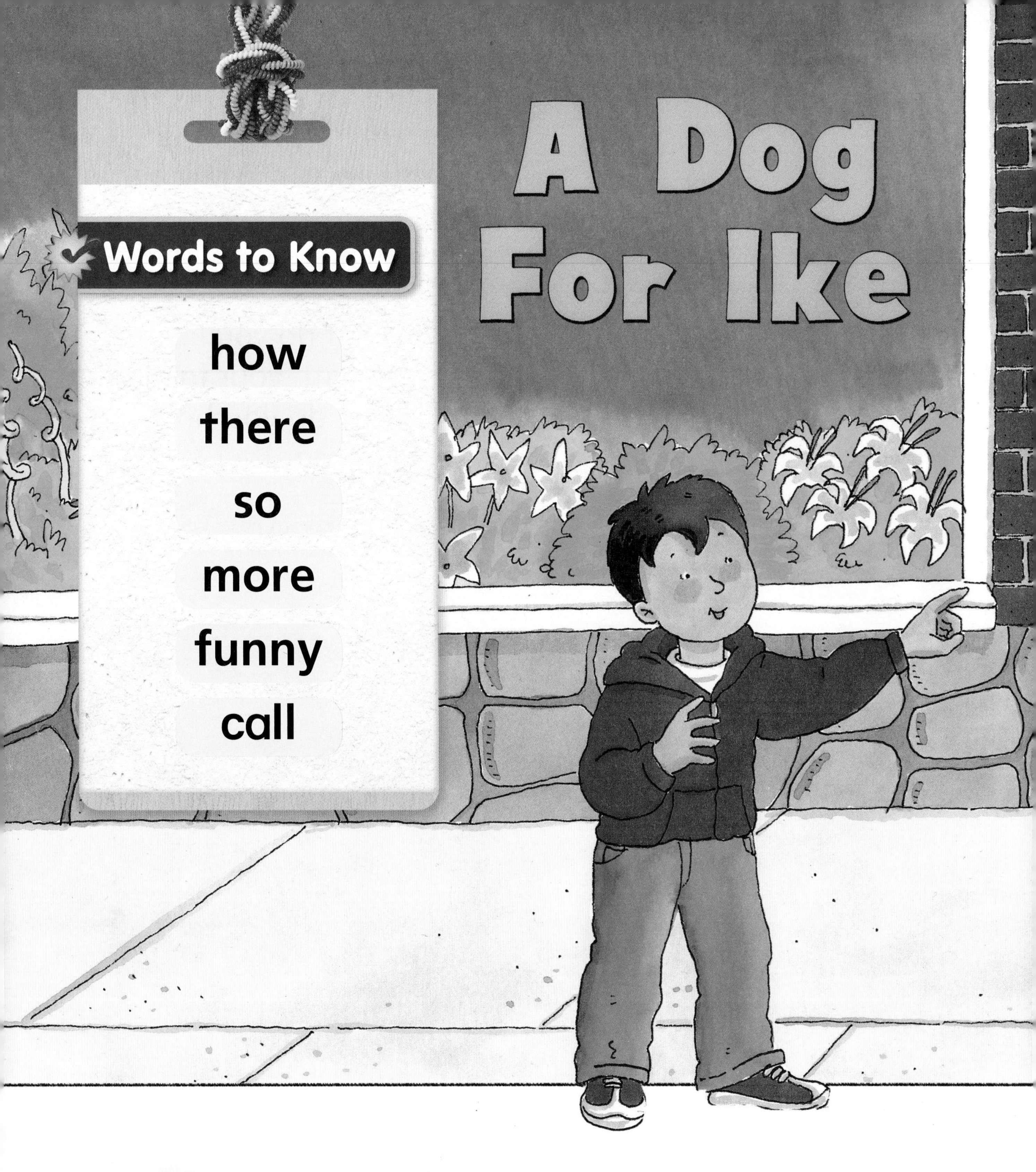

Ike: **How** will we pick out the best dog for us? **There** are **so** many dogs in the shop!

Dad: We will take our time. We will see one that we like **more** than the rest.

Ike: I like this **funny** little dog!
I think he likes me, too!

Mom: Then this must be the one.

Mom: He looks like a fine dog to me.

Ike: Let's **call** him Wags!

CA Comprehension

Genre
A Play is a story that can be acted out.

Story Structure
Make Predictions
Use your **Predictions Chart.**

What I Predict	What Happens

Read to Find Out
Who will make Mike smile?

Smile, Mike!

A Play

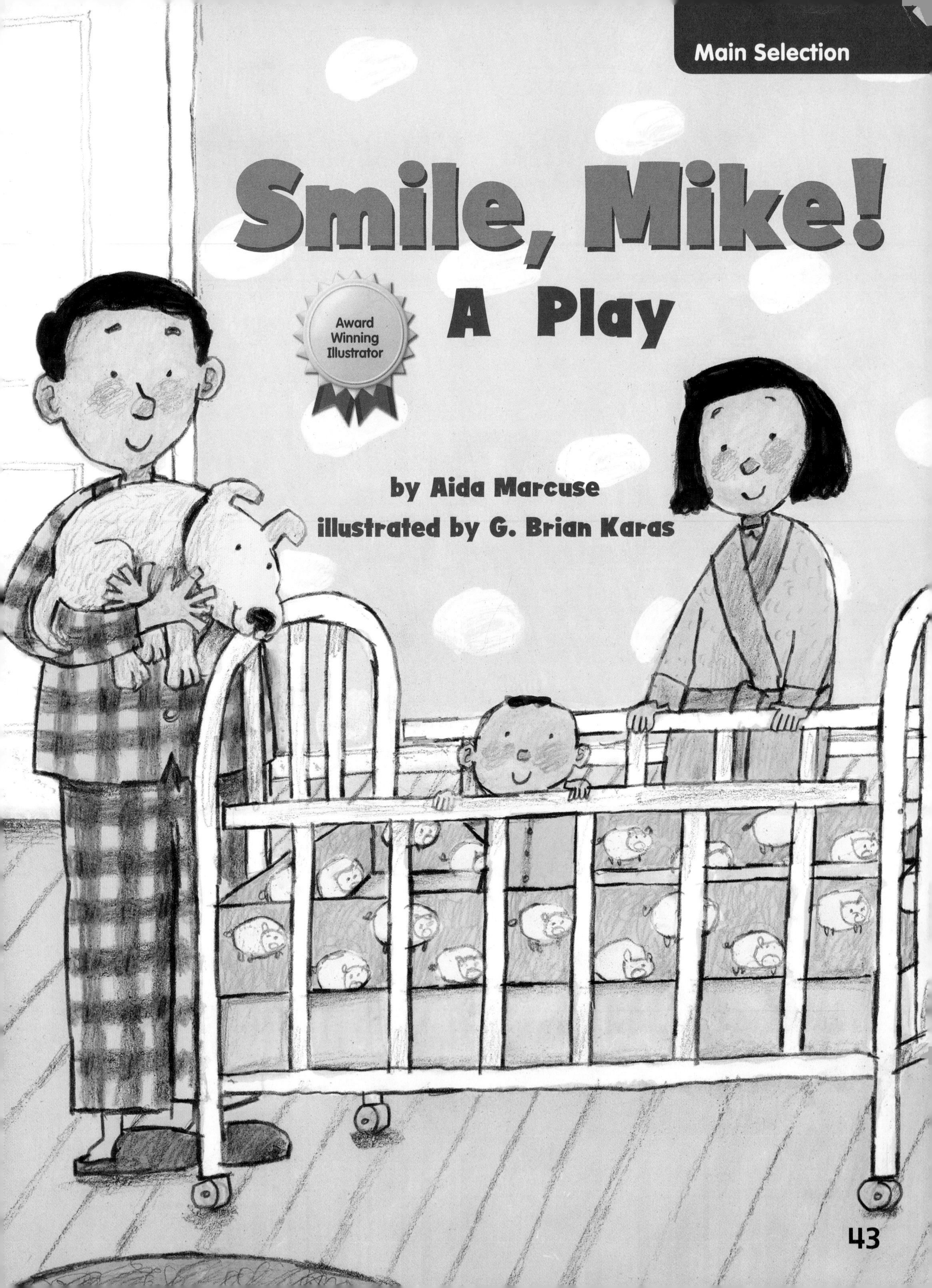

Award Winning Illustrator

by Aida Marcuse

illustrated by G. Brian Karas

Meet the Characters

Mike

Spike

Juan

Ana

Mom

Dad

Gram

Pops

 **Mike:** Waaaah!

 **Mom:** Here we are, little Mike.

 **Dad:** Did you **call** us?
Do you want to eat?

 **Mom:** No, he just had a fine snack.

Mike: Waaaah!

Ana: Why is Mike **so** sad?

Juan: Let's make him happy.
Do you want this cat, Mike?

Mike: No! No! No cat!

 **Ana:** Let's sing. **A - B - C - D - E - F - G - H - I -**

 **Dad:** **J - K - L - M - N - O - P -**

 **Juan:** **Q - R - S - T - U - V - W - X - Y - Z.**

 **Mike:** No! No! No sing!

Gram: Why is our little Mike so sad?

Mike: Waaaah!

Pops: **How** can we make him smile?

Gram: Let's clap hands!

Pops: Clap with us, Mike.

Mike: Waaah!

Gram: Clap hands with us.

Mike: No! No! No clap!

Ana: This **funny** duck will make Mike smile.

Mike: Waaah!

Mom: Do not be sad, Mike. Quack with us. Quack! Quack!

Mike: No! No! No quack!

 **Dad:** Look, Mike! I can make bubbles!

 **Mike:** Waaah!

 **Gram:** And I can get a bubble.

 **Mike:** No! No! No bubbles!

 **Ana:** Mike, look at my funny duck.

 **Mike:** Waaah!

 **Juan:** And look at my little cat.

 **Gram:** Look at me, Mike.

 **Mike:** Waaah!

 **Dad:** Look! **There** are **more** bubbles!

 **Pops:** Look, Mike! There is Spike.

 **Mike:** Waaah!

 **Juan:** Did you come to see Mike, Spike?

 **Ana:** Spike wants to make Mike smile.

Gram: Look at Spike spin.

Ana: Spike is funny!

Gram: Look! Mike has a big smile.

Pops: Spike made Mike smile.

 **Juan:** Good dog! This is for you, Spike.

 **Dad:** Show us how you can jump.

 **Mike:** Jump, Spike! Jump!

 **Spike:** Ruff! Ruff!

 **Dad:** At last, Mike is happy.

 **Mom:** Now it is time for bed.

 **Ana:** Mike will get some rest now.

 **Gram:** And so will we!

READ TOGETHER

Smile with Aida Marcuse!

Aida Marcuse says, "I wrote *Smile, Mike!* because mothers always try to make their children happy. I remember the day when my little boy wouldn't stop crying. At last we discovered what he wanted! I hope you enjoy reading this play. I enjoyed writing it!"

Find out more about Aida Marcuse at **www.macmillanmh.com**.

Author's Purpose

Aida Marcuse wanted to write about making a sad boy smile. What makes you smile? Write about it.

Critical Thinking

Retell the Story

Use the Retelling Cards to retell the story in order.

Retelling Cards

Think and Compare

What I Predict	What Happens

1. What do you think Mike's family will do the next time he cries?
2. How is Mike's family like your family?
3. What are some other ways you can make a baby smile and laugh?
4. How is Wags in "A Dog for Ike" like Spike?

READ TOGETHER

Healthy Eating

Science

Genre
Nonfiction gives information about a topic.

Text Feature
A Chart can show information in rows and columns.

Content Vocabulary
healthful
foods
energy

LOG ON Find out more about family activities at www.macmillanmh.com.

What are some foods your family likes to eat?

My family likes to eat **healthful foods**. Healthful foods give us **energy** to walk, work, and have fun.

Mom and Dad buy foods that are good for our family to eat. They pick healthful foods like milk, bread, meat, fish, fruits, and vegetables. Grains give us energy. Meat and fish help our muscles grow.

My family likes to help cook our food. I like to wash the vegetables. Grandmother chops them. Then I put them in a big bowl. We made a salad!

My family made fish, carrots, and rice. They are all healthful foods. They taste good, too!

What healthful foods does your family like to eat?

CA Critical Thinking

Think about the family in *Smile, Mike!* What healthful snacks could they make for Mike? Look at the chart on page 61 for ideas.

CA **Writing**

Present-Tense Verbs

Some verbs tell about actions that happen now.

Make a Poster

Amy made a poster about a play.

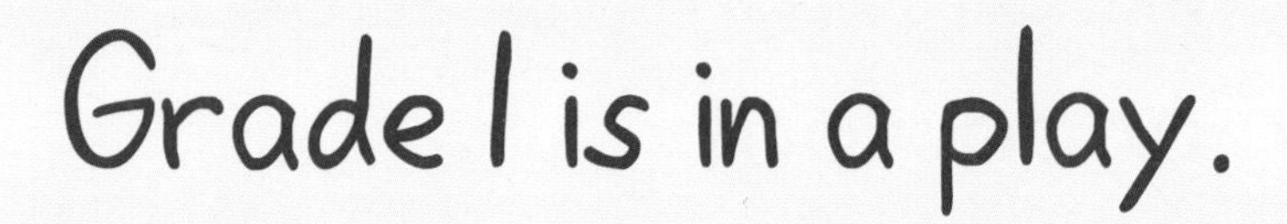

Grade 1 is in a play.

We sing and dance.

We are so funny!

Come see it.

Your Turn

Suppose your class is putting on a play. Think about what is special about the play. Make a poster telling people why the play is special.

Writer's Checklist

- ☑ Is my poster easy to read?
- ☑ Does my poster tell why the play is special?
- ☑ Did I use **verbs** that tell what happens now?

CA Talk About It

What types of art do you know about? What kind of art do you like to make?

LOG ON Find out more about making art at **www.macmillanmh.com**.

TIME FOR KIDS®

Making Art

Make A Doll

Words to Know

people
every
from
your
into
soon

Dolls are like **people**.
They come in **every** size
and shape.

What do you think
this doll was made **from**?
Yes! It was made from
a bit of cloth.

You can make a doll with **your** sock. Put some fluff **into** the sock. Then stitch it up. **Soon** you can play with your doll!

Comprehension

Genre

Nonfiction

A nonfiction article tells about real people and things.

Summarize

Main Idea and Details

Look for details that give information about masks.

Masks! Masks! Masks!

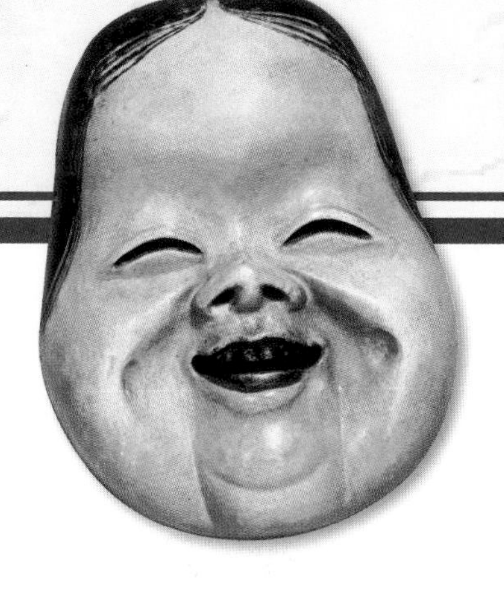

A mask hides **your** face. When you put on a mask, you can act out a story. You can act as if you are not yourself.

People make masks in **every** land.
Masks help them tell tales.
And masks help them have fun.

This mask is **from** Africa. What shapes can you see on the mask? Which animal is on top?

The masks on this page are from Japan. People use them when they act in plays. What tales could they tell with such masks?

Look at this bird. How do you think this mask was made? What is it made out of?

It takes much skill to make such a mask.

This mask is from Peru. It is shaped like the sun. Look at it. Can you see snakes?

Make a Mask

You can make a mask, too! First, get a plate. Cut holes **into** it. Check that you can see.

Next, color the mask. Paste fun things on it. **Soon** you will have a mask!

Last, tape a band on the back of the mask. Put the mask on. Who are you?

 Critical Thinking

Tell What You Learned

What did you learn about making masks?

Think and Compare

1. What is the main idea of the article?
2. Have you ever worn a mask? What did it look like?
3. What are some ways people use masks?
4. Would you rather make a sock doll or a mask? Why?

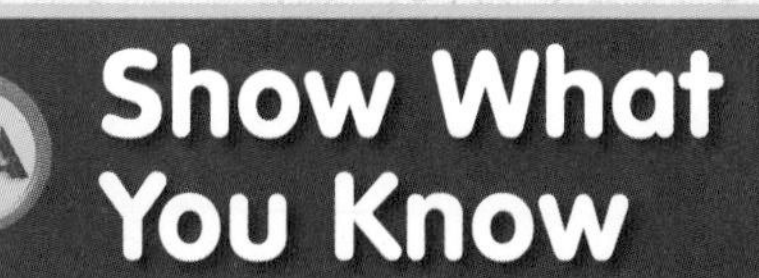

Show What You Know

Think and Search
Find the answer in more than one place.

Art in Caves

In 1940, four boys saw a hole in the ground. It was a cave.

The boys went in. They saw pictures on the walls. The pictures showed people and animals. There were birds, fish, horses, and bulls.

The boys told people about the caves. Scientists came. They said the pictures were thousands of years old. They showed how early people lived.

Go on

TIME
FOR KIDS

Directions: Answer the questions.

1 In what kind of place were the paintings found?

A

B

C

2 The cave was found by

A scientists.

B four boys.

C a cat.

Tip
Keep reading to find the answer.

3 The people who painted the cave paintings

A lived a long time ago.

B are still alive today.

C lived in 1940.

STOP

Write an Invitation

Anthony wrote an invitation to an art show.

Art Show!

Come to our art show.
It is on Friday in Ms. Rick's room.
We painted animals.
They are so funny!

CA Your Writing Prompt

Plan an art show for your class. Write an invitation. Tell about the show.

Then write when and where the show will be.

Writing Hints

- ☑ Plan what your invitation will say.
- ☑ Tell when and where the show will be.
- ☑ Check your work for mistakes.

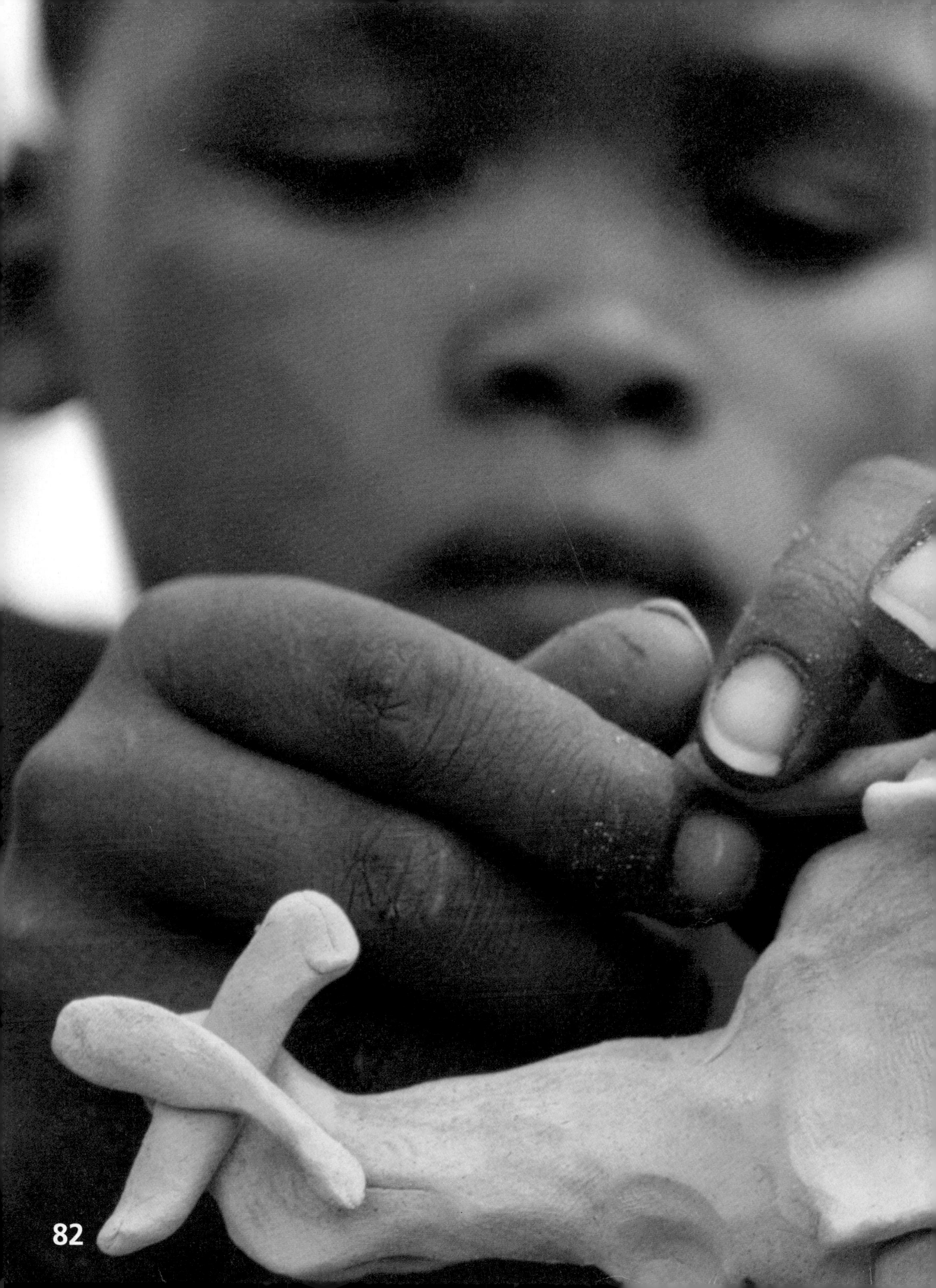

CA Talk About It

What does it mean to be creative? How are you creative?

LOG ON Find out more about being creative at **www.macmillanmh.com**.

Being Creative

Words to Know

done

old

new

find

work

after

The Old Box

"I am **done** with this **old** box," said Mom.

"Let's save it! We can make a **new** thing with it," said Kim.

"OK," said Mom. "I hope you **find** a good way to use it!"

Kim and Luke went to **work**.
"We can drive this when it's done," said Luke.

After it was done, Kim and Luke got in. They played with it for a long time. They had fun!

Rose

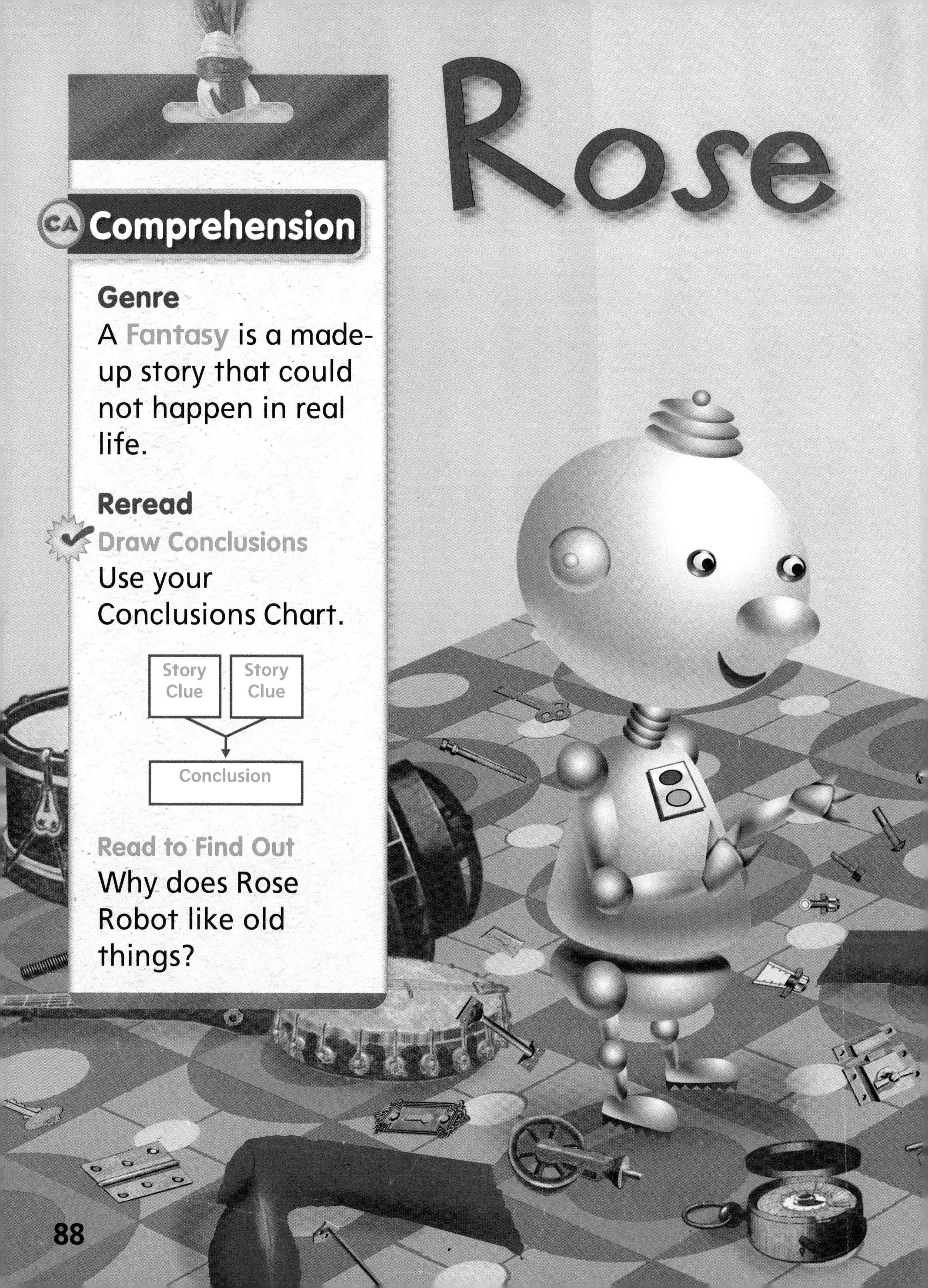

Comprehension

Genre

A **Fantasy** is a made-up story that could not happen in real life.

Reread

Draw Conclusions

Use your Conclusions Chart.

Read to Find Out

Why does Rose Robot like old things?

Robot Cleans Up

by Mary Anderson
illustrated by Michael Garland

Rose Robot liked to **find old** things.
Her little brother Rob liked to help.

"Rose, what will we do with this old junk?" asked Rob.

"We will use it," said Rose.

They passed Luke and his dad.

"This stuff broke," said Luke. "We are bringing it to the dump."

"But it is such good stuff!" said Rose. "I can use it."

Luke gave his old stuff to Rose.

Rose and Rob went home.

"Rose, is that more old stuff?" asked her mom.

"What will you do with that junk?" asked her dad.

"I am going to use it," said Rose.

Rose went to her room.

"Come and help me, Rob," she said. "I will make a **new** toy for you to jump in."

Soon Rose was **done**.

"Get in, Rob," she said.

"Rose! Look at me jump!" said Rob. "You make the best things."

"What is that thumping?" asked Mom.

"What is going on up there?" asked Dad.

"Let's go find out," they said.

“Rob! Stop that jumping!” said Mom.

“Rose! Look at this mess,” said Dad.

Then Mom and Dad spoke together. “We must get rid of all this junk,” they said.

"But this is such good stuff!" said Rose.
"Look! I made this for reading in bed."

"And she made this for me to play a
tune on!" said Rob.

"Very cute," said Mom. "But this mess has to go!"

"Tomorrow we will bring the things you can't use to the dump," said Dad.

After Mom and Dad left, Rose looked at her stuff.

"Rob, I have a plan," said Rose. "I can have a clean room and still keep my stuff."

"Can I help?" asked Rob.

Rose and Rob went to **work**.

"We can use so much of this stuff," said Rose.

"I hope Mom and Dad like this!" said Rob.

Rose and Rob worked and worked.

At last, they were done. Rose smiled.

"This is my best thing yet," she said.

"I'll get Mom and Dad," said Rob.

“Mom and Dad!” said Rob. “Look at what we made.”

“What is it?” they asked.

“You’ll see,” said Rose. “I just have to pull this switch.”

"Your room is so clean!" said Mom.

"And you used so much old stuff," said Dad.

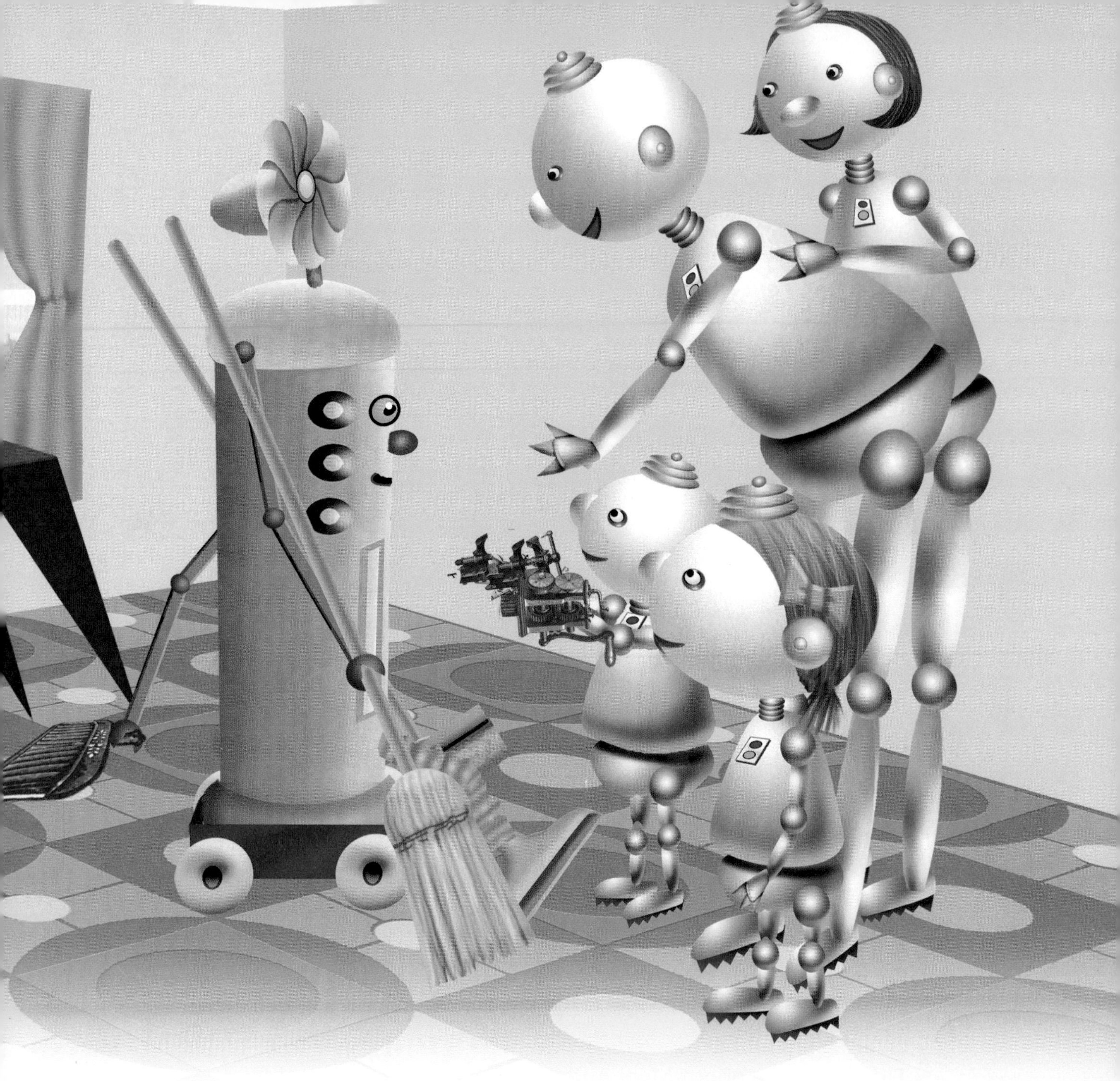

“Look!” said Rob. “This is the stuff we didn’t use. You can bring it to the dump.”

“But Rose can make something new with it,” said Mom and Dad.

“I can!” said Rose.

Read Together

Who Made Rose Robot?

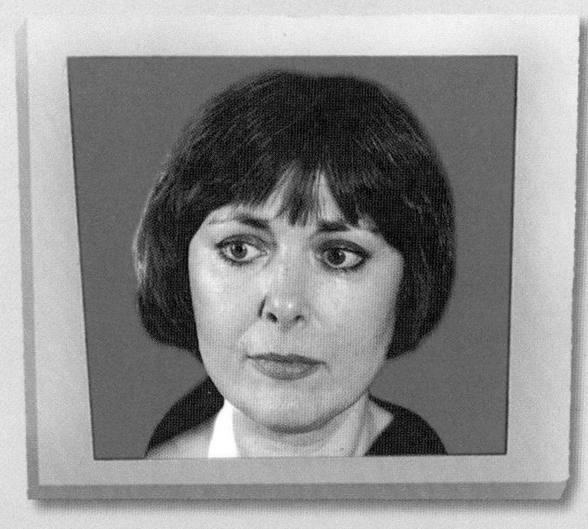

Mary Anderson says, "I am just like Rose Robot. I love to find old stuff. My home is filled with things I have found and fixed up."

Michael Garland paints, draws, and uses a computer to make his pictures.

Other books by Michael Garland

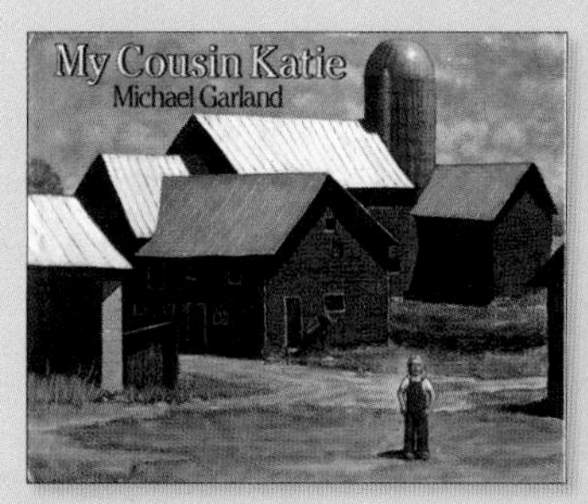

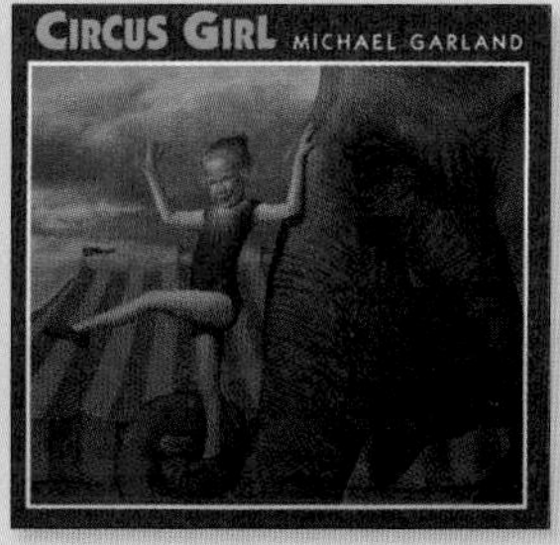

LOG ON Find out more about Mary Anderson and Michael Garland at **www.macmillanmh.com**.

CA Author's Purpose

Mary Anderson tells about an unusual machine. Write about a machine you'd like to make.

Critical Thinking

Retell the Story

Use the Retelling Cards to retell the story in order.

Retelling Cards

Think and Compare

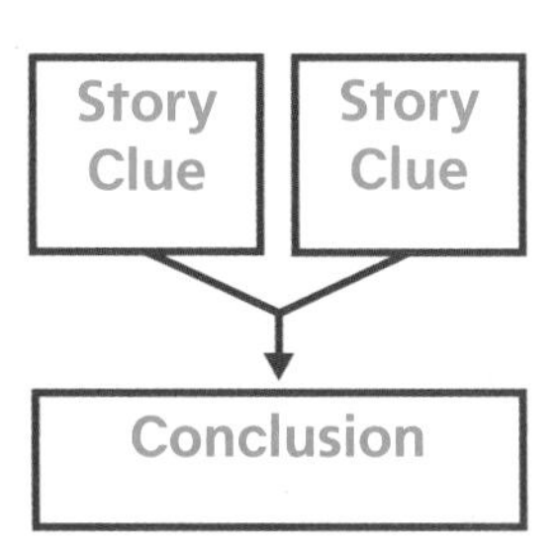

1. What will Mom and Dad do the next time Rose brings junk home?
2. Would you like to have a friend like Rose? Why or why not?
3. What kind of robot would you make? What would it do?
4. How is Rose Robot like Kim and Luke in "The Old Box"?

CA

History/ Social Science

Genre

Nonfiction gives information about a topic.

Text Feature

A Floor Plan is a drawing that shows where things are in a room.

Content Vocabulary

recycling

sort

plastic

LOG ON Find out more about recycling at **www.macmillanmh.com**.

READ TOGETHER

A Bottle Takes a Trip

Ahh! You just drank some water. Now you toss the bottle in a blue bin for **recycling**. What will happen to that bottle?

A truck will come to pick up your bottle. It will go with many bottles to a recycling center.

When they get there, the bottles go down a big slide.

Now people **sort** the cans, bottles, and paper.

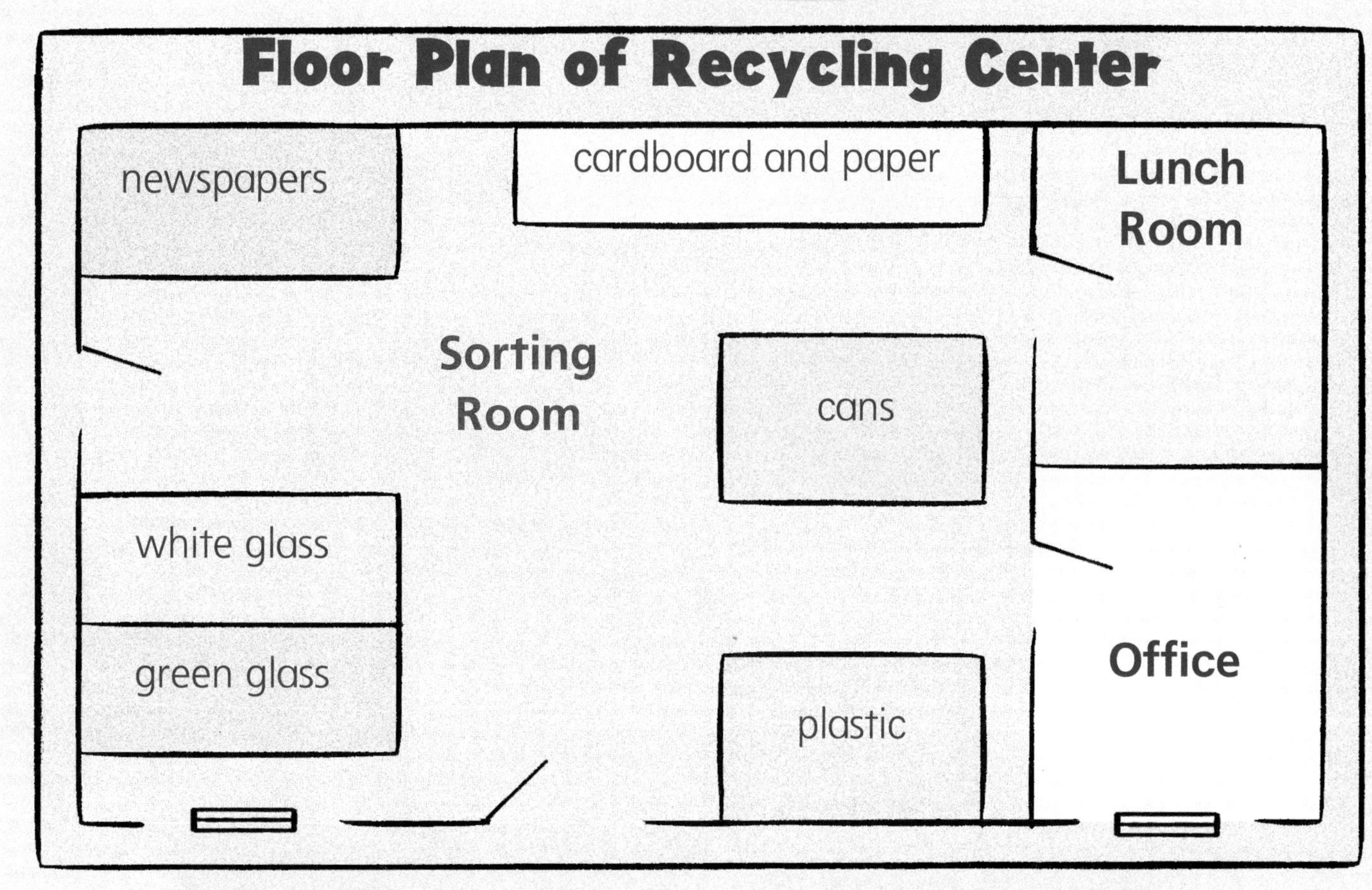

Look at this floor plan of a recycling center. What kinds of things do you see being recycled?

Your bottle is made of **plastic**.
It will go to a factory. Here the bottles are cut up into small bits.

Next the plastic bits are melted until they are soft. The soft plastic can be used to make many new things.

The green rulers on this page were made from recycled plastic. Recycled plastic can also be made into yarn. It can be used to make socks and sweaters and to fill sleeping bags.

All of the things this girl has were made out of recycled plastic. One of them could have come from your bottle!

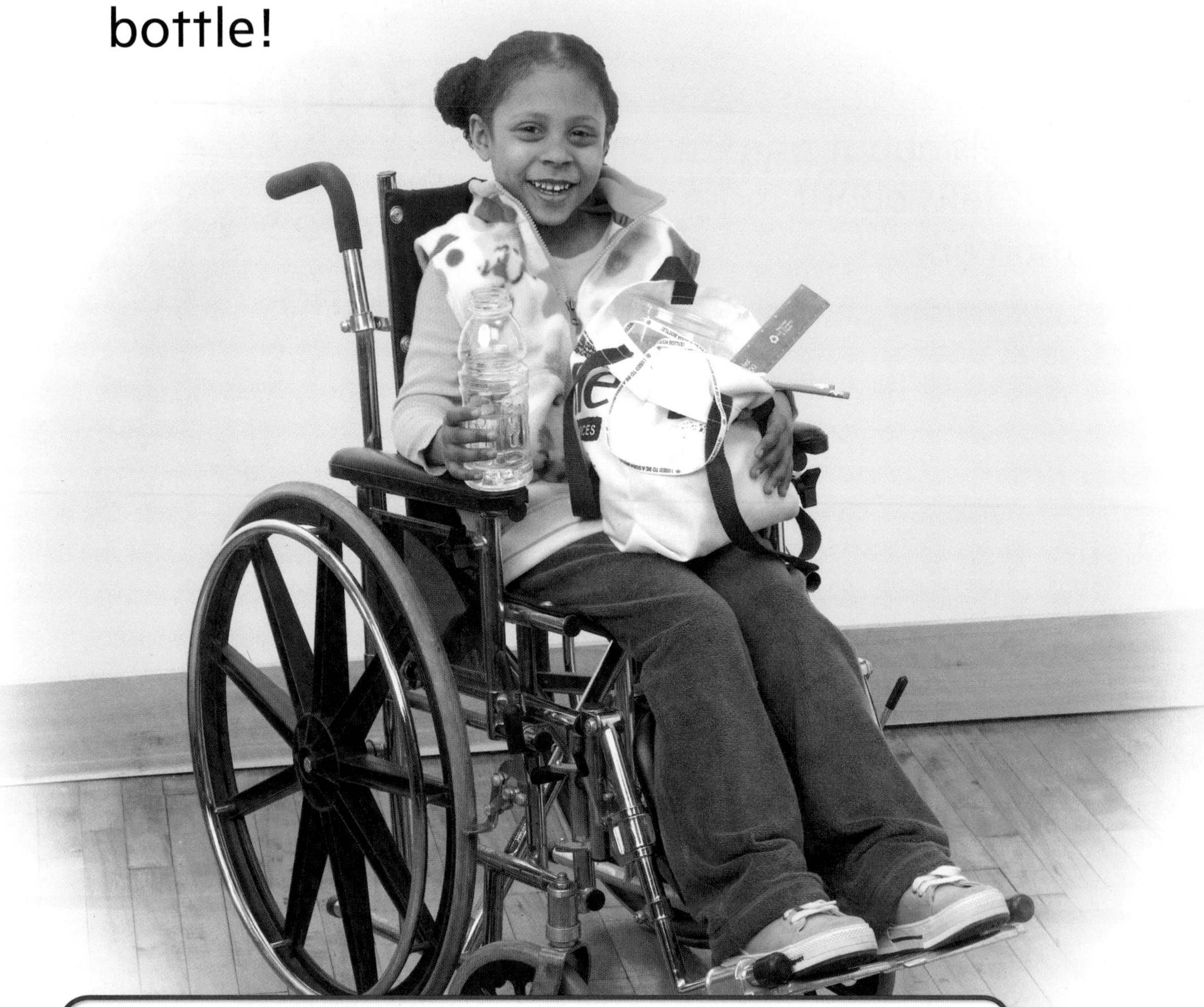

Critical Thinking

Rose Robot makes new things out of old things. How is this like the recycling in "A Bottle Takes a Trip"?

Writing

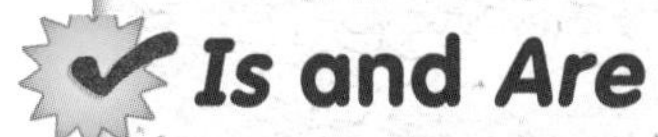

Is* and *Are

Is tells about one.
Are tells about more than one.

Write About Making a New Thing

Ramon wrote about making a drum.

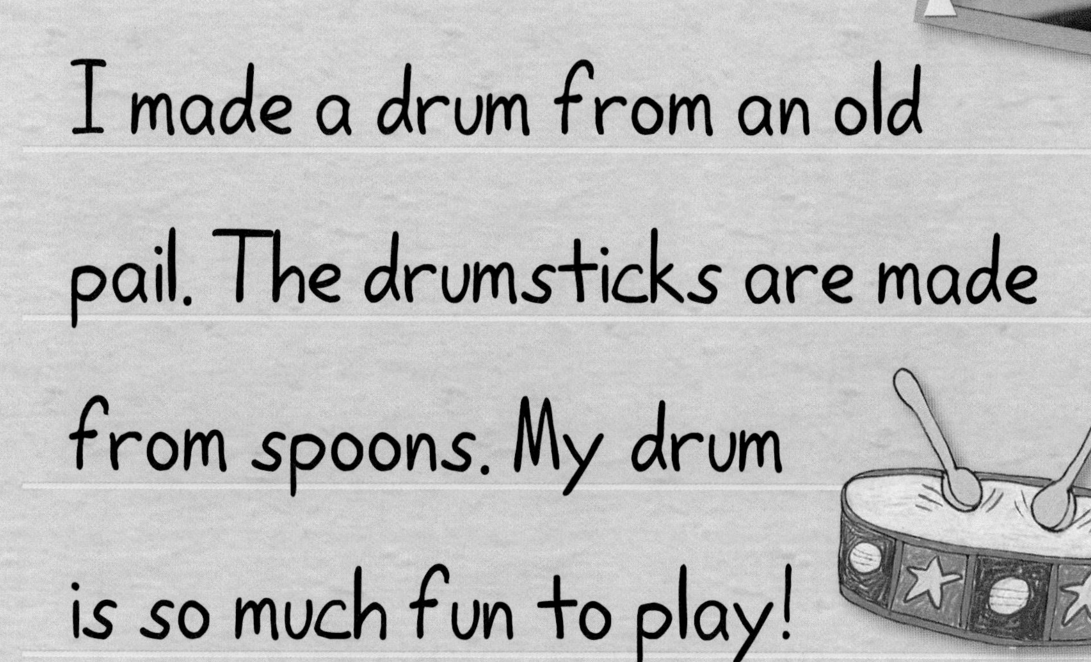

I made a drum from an old pail. The drumsticks are made from spoons. My drum is so much fun to play!

Your Turn

What could you make from something old?

Write about it.

Tell how you could make it.

Writer's Checklist

- Did I describe what I would like to make?

- Did I use **is** and **are** correctly?

- Does my exclamation end with an exclamation mark?

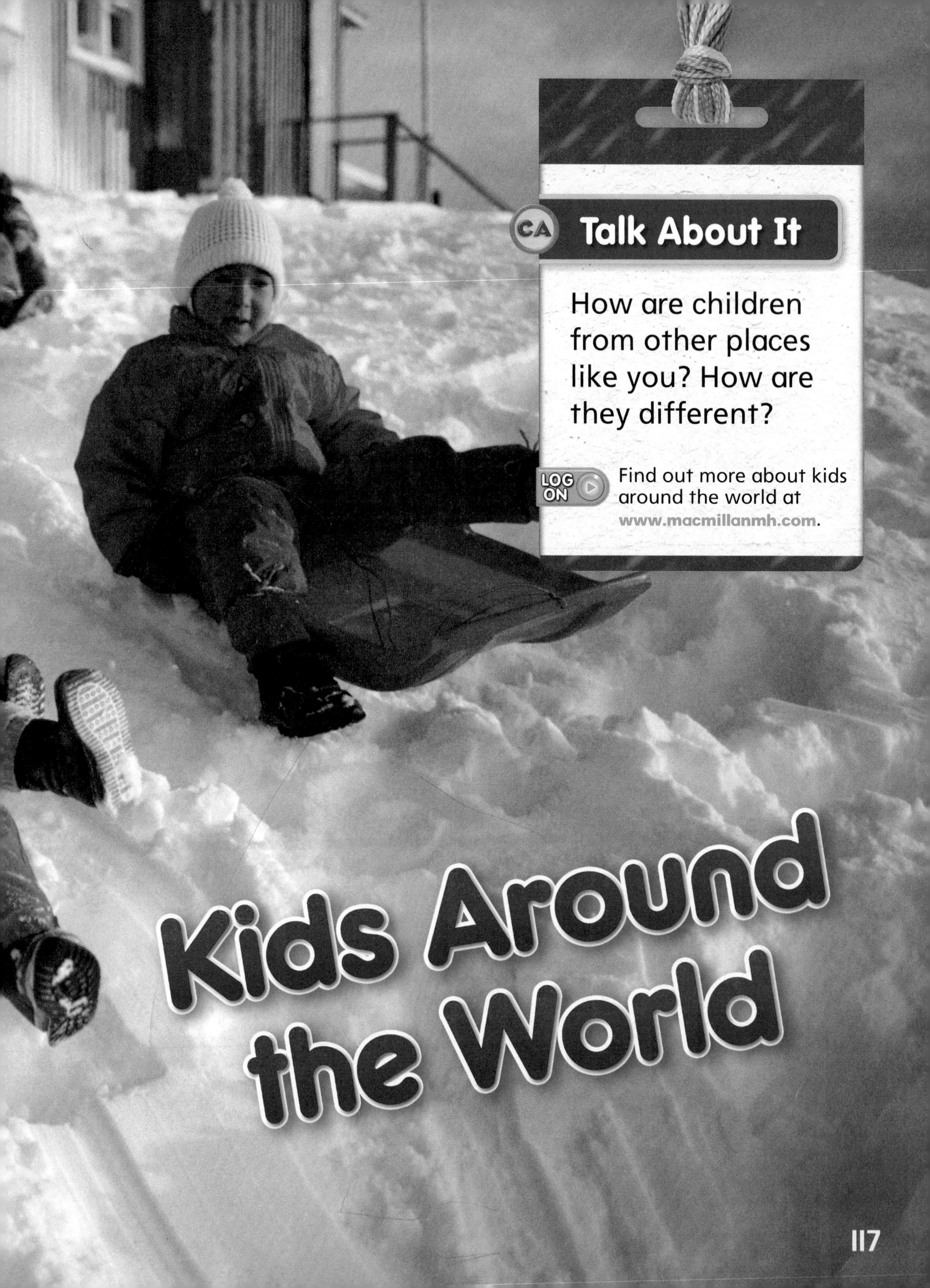

CA **Talk About It**

How are children from other places like you? How are they different?

LOG ON Find out more about kids around the world at www.macmillanmh.com.

Kids Around the World

Words to Know

boy

does

any

water

girl

by

friends

It's Fun to Help

Kids all over like to help.
This **boy** **does** the dishes.
He scrubs and scrubs.
Will he spill **any** **water**?

This **girl** helps her mom bake.
It smells good! It will taste
good, too.

This boy digs and digs. He will make a path. He likes to do it **by** himself.

These **friends** help with old cans and glass. They put them into bins.

Helping out is fun! How do you like to help?

Comprehension

Genre

Nonfiction tells about real people and things.

Text Structure

Compare and Contrast

Use your Compare and Contrast Chart.

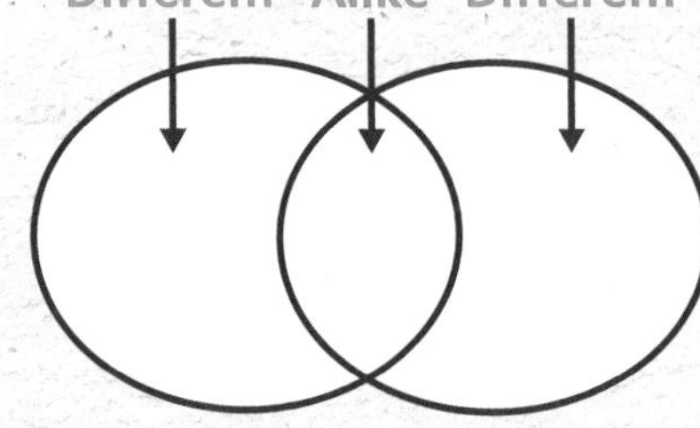

Read to Find Out

How do kids around the world have fun?

Kids Have Fun!

By Minda Novek

Kids have fun in every land. They have fun doing many things.

It's fun to play games. Kids in this icy land like to jump rope.

This **boy** plays a game with a flat bat.
Will he strike the ball?
Do you play **any** games with a bat?

It's fun to move.
This **girl** has lots of fun with a hoop.
When she swings her hips,
the hoop spins.

This boy **does** tricks with a rope.
He can make a ring with it.
Then he jumps into it and out again.

It is fun to make things!
This boy cuts up scraps.
Snip, snip!
What shape did he make?

This girl makes things from leaves.
She cuts them in strips.
She will use them to make a box.

It's fun to make things up.
This boy acts like a lion.
He shakes his mane.
But then he smiles.

These kids like to make up games.
They made a ship.
They used sticks, cloth, and a box.

It's fun to see new things.
This boy finds new things under **water**.
Look at what he picked up!

What does this boy see?
It is wide.
How wide can he stretch?

It's fun to learn new things.
This girl's mom shows her
how to make a rug out of string.

This boy's dad shows him how to
make pots.
They have fun doing it together.

Holidays are fun!
This boy is all dressed up.
He has a mask.
He acts strong.

These kids get dressed up for a holiday.
Then they have fun dancing.
It's fun to see them, too!

It's fun to do things with **friends**.
When two kids play like this,
can they go fast?

It's fun to do things **by** yourself.
Just sitting and thinking can be fun.
This girl likes to read.

Lots of things are fun.
How do you have fun?

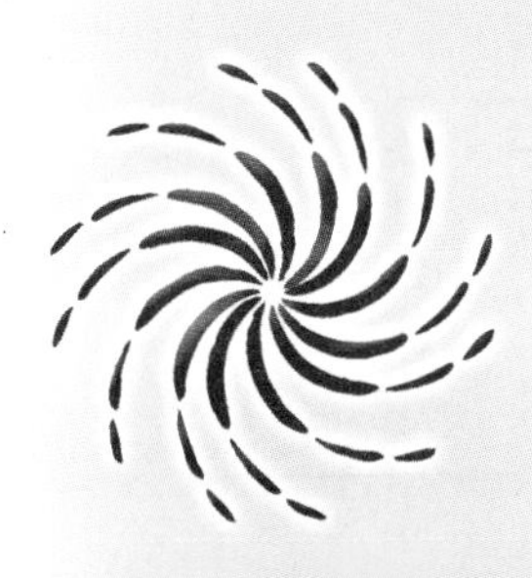

Minda Novek's World

Minda Novek says, "In my books, I like to write about how people live all over the world. I use pictures of real people. I try to show how their lives are like yours and how they are different, too."

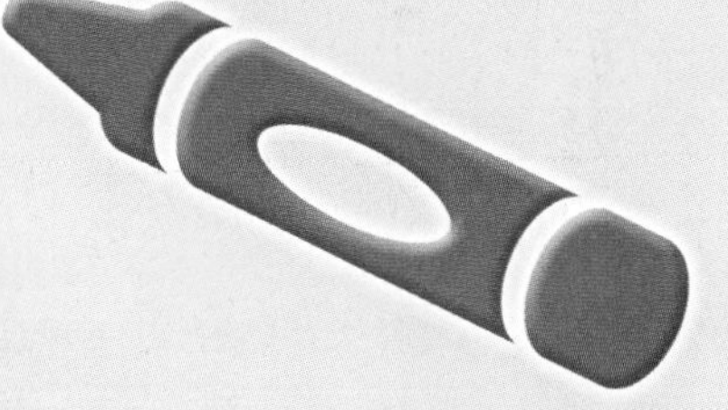

LOG ON
Find out more about Minda Novek at www.macmillanmh.com.

CA Author's Purpose

Minda Novek likes to write about kids all over the world. Pick a kid from *Kids Have Fun!* Write about how you two could have fun together.

Critical Thinking

Retell the Story

Use the Retelling Cards to retell the selection in order.

Retelling Cards

Think and Compare

1. Look at pages 126 and 127. How are the girl and boy playing in the same way? How are they playing differently?

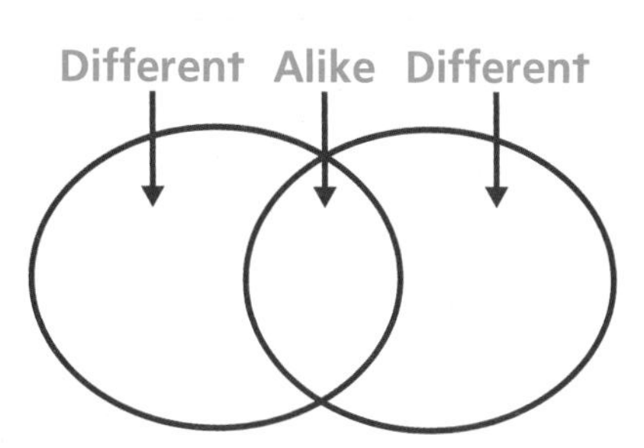

2. How do you like to have fun?
3. Do kids from different places have fun the same way you do? How?
4. How are *Kids Have Fun!* and "It's Fun to Help" the same?

CA

Poetry

Genre
Poems use words in imaginative ways.

Literary Element
Word Choice is important in a poem. Poets often choose interesting words to write about everyday things.

LOG ON Find out more about kids around the world at www.macmillanmh.com.

READ TOGETHER

Kids' Poems From Around the World

Kids everywhere write poetry. These kids found new ways to write about the sky, the sea, and the sun.

The Sky Is Busy

The lighthouse
On that island
Is shining.
Helicopters in the sky
Are shining.
Boats are glittering, too.
And with a bang
Someone is shooting
off fireworks.
Today the sky
Is very busy.

Ishikawa Mwumi,
Kindergarten, Japan

The Sea

The mist smudges out
Kapiti Island

the hills curve and rise
like loaves of bread

the sun sprinkles glitter
on the sea

the wind is writing what it knows
in lines along the water.

Laura Ranger, age 7,
New Zealand

Sun Rise

Sun, sun, sun
Rise up from the clouds
Spread your rays
Flowers will be happy
Birds will sing
And I shall be happy
and sing, too.

Camille Pabalan,
age 6, Canada

Critical Thinking

Choose a child from *Kids Have Fun*. What might this child write a poem about?

CA

Writing

Contractions

A **contraction** is a short form of two words.

do + not = don't

Write About Fun at School

Wren wrote about playing statues.

I like to play statues.
When Miss Chan tells us to
stop, we don't move.
It's hard not to laugh!

Your Turn

How do you have fun
at school?

Write about it.

Tell what you do
and why you like it.

Writer's Checklist

- Did I write about fun at school?

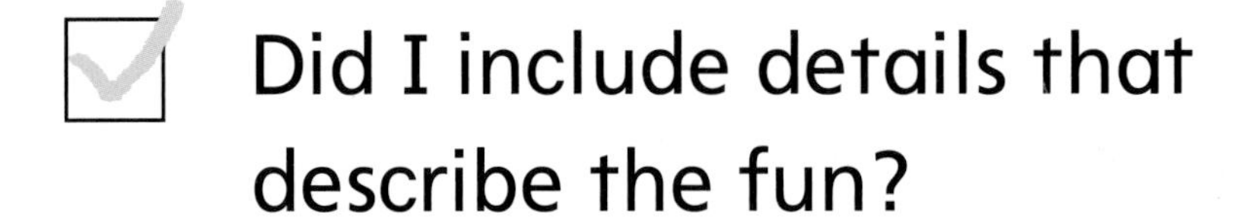

- Did I include details that describe the fun?

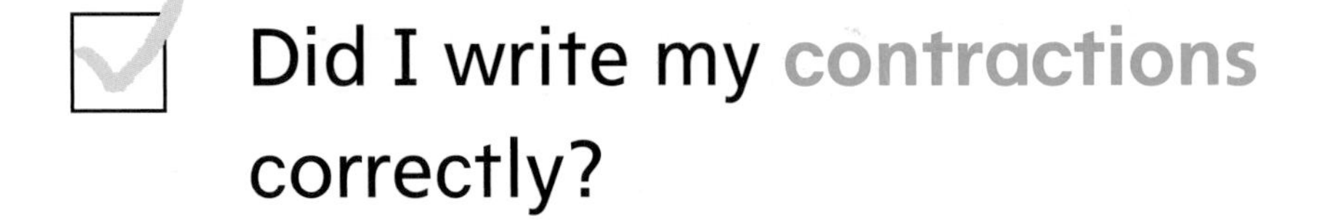

- Did I write my **contractions** correctly?

Review

- Make Predictions
- Main Idea and Details
- Photographs
- Labels

Kate: Can you play with me, June?

June: OK. But I don't have much time.

Kate: I 'd like to swing in the park.

June: It takes such a long time to get there.

Kate: What do you want to do?

June: I want to ride bikes.

Kate: If we ride, we can get to the park fast.

June: Good thinking, Kate.

Kate: Now we can swing and ride!

Read Together

Made at Home

Today, kids shop for toys and games. What did kids do long ago? A lot of kids made toys at home. They used things they could find.

Kids made kites at home. They used bags, sticks, and string.

Kids made dolls from cloth. They cut out shapes. They stuffed them with rags. Then they stitched them up. Kids made dolls from lots of things. They even used corn husks!

Today kids hit balls with a bat. A long time ago kids made bats from big sticks. What did they call the game? They called it stick ball!

homemade kite

corn husk doll

Critical Thinking

Now answer the questions. Base your answers on the story "Kate and June."

1 What does Kate want to do first?

A jump rope

B swing in the park

C ride bikes

2 Why is Kate so happy to ride bikes?

A She wanted to ride bikes.

B She can get to the park quickly to swing.

C She can ride to the store to buy things.

3 What did you predict Kate and June would do? What did they do? Write about it.

Now answer the questions. Base your answers on the story "Made at Home."

1 What is this story mainly about?

A toys kids made long ago

B toys kids make now

C making dolls

2 Which toy has a label?

A train

B rag doll

C corn husk doll

Write on Demand

PROMPT How are the toys in the pictures different from the toys kids have today? Write as much as you can and as well as you can.

Glossary

What Is a Glossary?

A glossary can help you find the meanings of words. The words are listed in alphabetical order. You can look up a word and read it in a sentence. There is a picture to help you.

old

friends

Sample Entry

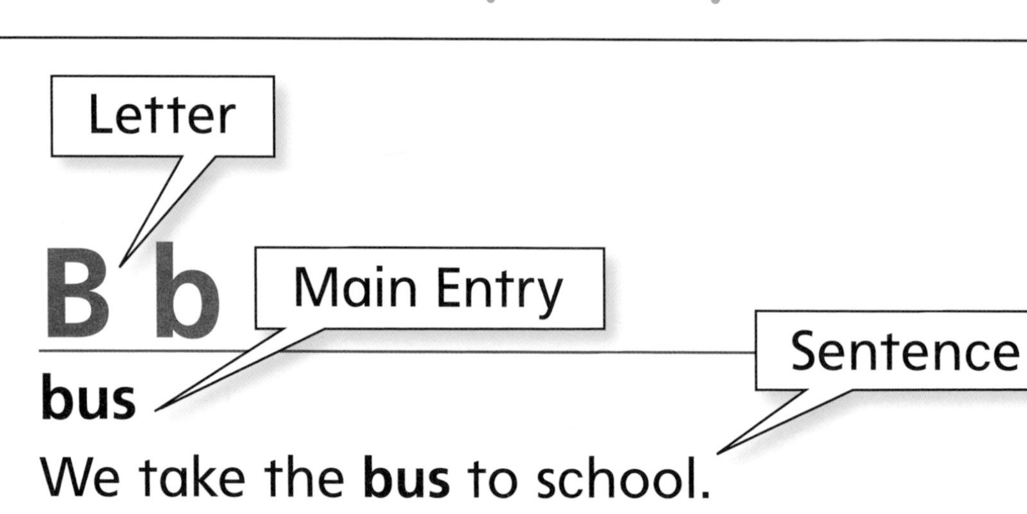

duck

Bb

boy

This **boy** likes to jump rope.

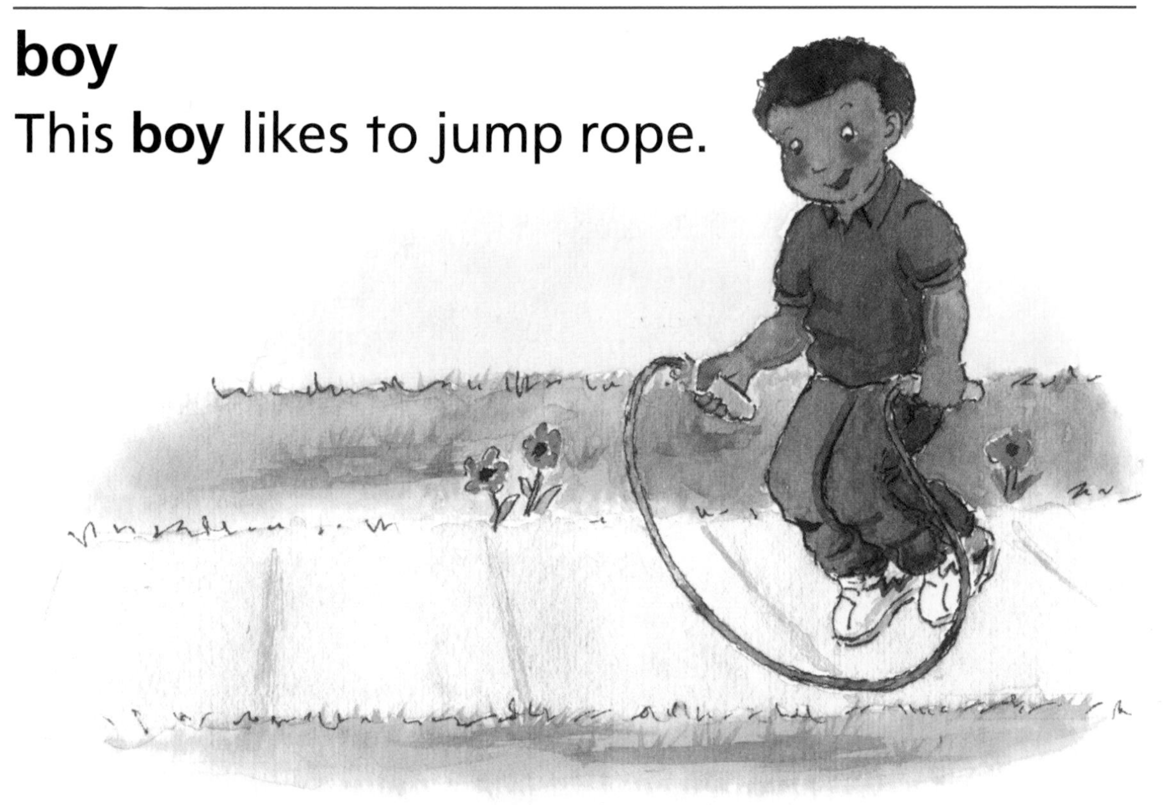

bubbles

The **bubbles** are colorful.

bus

We take the **bus** to school.

Cc

cute

Meg has a **cute** kitten.

Dd

duck

The **duck** is floating on the pond.

Ff

friends

I have fun with my **friends**.

Ll

lake

The boat is on the **lake**.

like

Most cats don't **like** dogs.

Mm

make

Grace can **make** dolls from old socks.

Oo

old

This radio is very **old**.

Pp

path

We walk on the **path**.

plastic

I have a **plastic** lunch box.

Rr

rope

Rose and Jess can climb a **rope**.

Ss

scrubs

Scott **scrubs** the dishes.

Tt

together

Katie and Matt build **together**.

Ww

wig

I wear a **wig**.

Acknowledgments

The publisher gratefully acknowledges permission to reprint the following copyrighted material:

"The Sea" by Laura Ranger from poems from *Stone Soup Magazine* May/June 1993 issue. Copoyright © 2005 by Stone Soup, Santa Cruz, CA 95063.

"The Sky is Busy" by Ishikawa Megumi © 1993 from *Festival in My Heart: Poems by Japanese Children*, Harry N. Abrams, Incorporated, NY, A Times Mirror Corporations. Reprinted with permission from Harry N. Abrams, Inc., NY.

"Sun Rise" by Camille Pabalan from *KidzPage: Poetry and Verse for Children of All Ages*, November 2000, page 36, Tangled Lives. Copyright © 1998–2000 by Emmi Tarr.

Book Cover, MRS. BROWN WENT TO TOWN by Wong Herbert Yee. Copyright © 2003 by Wong Herbert Yee. Reprinted by permission of Houghton Mifflin.

Book Cover, CIRCUS GIRL by Michael Garland. Copyright © 1993 by Michael Garland. Used by permission of Dutton Children's Books, a division of Penguin Books USA Inc.

Book Cover, FIREMAN SMALL by Wong Herbert Yee. Copyright © 1994 by Wong Herbert Yee. Reprinted by permission of Houghton Mifflin Company.

ILLUSTRATIONS

Cover Illustration: Leland Klanderman

8-11: Vincent Nguyen. 12–29: Wong Herbert Yee. 30–33: Mircea Catusanu. 34: Ken Bowser. 35: Diane Paterson. 38–41: Anthony Lewis. 76: K. Michael Crawford. 80: Julia Woolf. 84–87: Josée Masse. 88–107: Michael Garland. 108–112: Jessica Wolk Stanley. 114: Daniel DelValle. 142–145: Tomek Bogacki. 146: Ken Bowser. 148–149: Elivia Savadier. 156: Carol Koeller. 159–160: Carol Koeller. 163: Janee Trasler.

PHOTOGRAPHY

All Photographs are by Ken Cavanagh or Ken Karp or Natalie Ray for Macmillan/McGraw-Hill (MMH) except as noted below.

Inside front & back covers: Medioimages/PunchStock. v: (t) The Art Archive/Neil Setchfield; (b) Sean Justice/Getty Images. 2-3: Bruno De Hogues/Getty Images. 3: Creatas Images. 4: Rubberball/PunchStock. 5: Courtesy of David Diaz. 6-7: Tim Fitzharris/Masterfile. 28: Courtesy of Wong Herbert Yee. 34: Bill Frymire/Masterfile. 36-37: Myrleen Ferguson Cate/Photo Edit. 58: Courtesy of Aida Marcuse. 60: ACE STOCK LIMITED/Alamy. 60-63: (bkgd) Wetzel and Company. 61: (t) D. Hurst/Alamy; (bcr) PhotoLink/Getty Images; (br) Digital Vision/Getty Images. 62: (t) Blend/PunchStock; (cr) John A. Rizzo/Getty Images; (bl) C Squared Studios/Getty Images. 63: Studio M/Stock Connection/Jupiter Images. 64: Ariel Skelly/CORBIS. 65: (tr) Hemera Technologies/Alamy; (tcr) Photodisc/Getty Images. 66-67: The Art Archive/Neil Setchfield. 68: Gail Vachon. 69: Jim Lane/Alamy. 70: (tr) Brooklyn Museum/CORBIS; (bl) Scala/Art Resource. 71: Jon Arnold Images/Alamy. 72: Giraudon/Art Resource. 73: Scala/Art Resource. 74: Frans Lanting/CORBIS. 75: Brooklyn Museum/CORBIS. 78: Maxppp/Zuma Press/Newscom. 79: (l to r) Stephen Alvarez/NGS Image Collection; Atlantide Phototravel/CORBIS; Lynne Reynolds/Brand X Pictures/Jupiter Images. 80: Royalty-Free/CORBIS. 81: Bet Noire/Shutterstock. 82-83: Anthony Bannister/CORBIS. 106: (tr) Courtesy of Mary Anderson; (cl) Courtesy of Michael Garland. 109: Javier Larrea/AGE Fotostock. 110: AP-Wide World Photos. 111 & 112: Richard Hutchings/Photo Edit. 114: LWA-Dann Tardif/CORBIS. 116-117: Bryan & Cherry Alexander Photography. 118: Van Hilversum/Alamy. 119: Paul Chesley/Getty Images. 120: David Morris/Alamy. 121: Bob Daemmrich/The Image Works. 122: Sean Justice/Getty Images. 124: Robert van der Hilst/CORBIS. 125: Karan Kapoor/Getty Images. 126: Digital Vision/Getty Images. 127: Lindsay Hebberd/CORBIS. 128: Photodisc/PunchStock. 129: Bob Krist/CORBIS. 130: Rebecca Emery/CORBIS. 131: Digital Vision/Getty Images. 132: Terje Rakke/Getty Images. 133: Randy Faris/CORBIS. 134: Paul Chesley/Getty Images. 135: Alvaro Leiva/AGE Fotostock. 136: Rodolfo Arpia/Alamy. 137: Robert Fried/Alamy. 138: Dennis MacDonald/AGE Fotostock. 139: Avril O'Reilly/Alamy. 140: Courtesy of Minda Novek. 146: Bohemian Nomad Picturemakers/CORBIS. 147: Nic Hamilton/Alamy. 150: Enzo & Paolo Ragazzini/CORBIS. 151: (t) C Squared Studios/Getty Images; (br) Sherman/Getty Images; (bc) David Lassman/Syracuse Newspapers/The Image Works. 154: (cl) Photodisc/Getty Images; (br) Laura Dwight/CORBIS. 155: (c) Gary Buss/Getty Images; (b) Getty Images. 156: Bill Hickey/Getty Images. 157: Gary Buss/Getty Images. 158: (t) Getty Images; (b) Tom & Dee Ann McCarthy/CORBIS. 159: Tim Davis/CORBIS. 160: Photodisc/Getty Images. 161: Stockbyte/Picture Quest. 162: (t) Joyce Choo/CORBIS; (b) Jennie Woodcock; Reflections Photolibrary/CORBIS. 163: Joseph Sohm; ChromoSohm Inc./CORBIS. CA Standards pages 1-4: Medioimages/PunchStock.

Reading/Language Arts
CA California Standards
Grade 1

READING

1.0 **Word Analysis, Fluency, and Systematic Vocabulary Development**
Students understand the basic features of reading. They select letter patterns and know how to translate them into spoken language by using phonics, syllabication, and word parts. They apply this knowledge to achieve fluent oral and silent reading.

Concepts About Print

1.1	Match oral words to printed words.
1.2	Identify the title and author of a reading selection.
1.3	Identify letters, words, and sentences.

Phonemic Awareness

1.4	Distinguish initial, medial, and final sounds in single-syllable words.
1.5	Distinguish long-and short-vowel sounds in orally stated single-syllable words (e.g., *bit/bite*).
1.6	Create and state a series of rhyming words, including consonant blends.
1.7	Add, delete, or change target sounds to change words (e.g., change *cow* to *how; pan* to *an*).
1.8	Blend two to four phonemes into recognizable words (e.g., */c/ a/ t/* = cat; */f/ l/ a/ t/* = flat).
1.9	Segment single-syllable words into their components (e.g., */c/ a/ t/* = cat; */s/ p/ l/ a/ t/* = splat; */r/ i/ ch/* = rich).

Decoding and Word Recognition

1.10	Generate the sounds from all the letters and letter patterns, including consonant blends and long-and short-vowel patterns (i.e., phonograms), and blend those sounds into recognizable words.
1.11	Read common, irregular sight words (e.g., *the, have, said, come, give, of*).
1.12	Use knowledge of vowel digraphs and *r*- controlled letter-sound associations to read words.
1.13	Read compound words and contractions.
1.14	Read inflectional forms (e.g., *-s, -ed, -ing*) and root words (e.g., *look, looked, looking*).
1.15	Read common word families (e.g., *-ite, -ate*).
1.16	Read aloud with fluency in a manner that sounds like natural speech.

Vocabulary and Concept Development	
1.17	Classify grade-appropriate categories of words (e.g., concrete collections of animals, foods, toys).

2.0 **Reading Comprehension**
Students read and understand grade-level-appropriate material. They draw upon a variety of comprehension strategies as needed (e.g., generating and responding to essential questions, making predictions, comparing information from several sources). The selections in *Recommended Literature, Kindergarten Through Grade Twelve* illustrate the quality and complexity of the materials to be read by students. In addition to their regular school reading, by grade four, students read one-half million words annually, including a good representation of grade-level-appropriate narrative and expository text (e.g., classic and contemporary literature, magazines, newspapers, online information). In grade one, students begin to make progress toward this goal.

Structural Features of Informational Materials	
2.1	Identify text that uses sequence or other logical order.

Comprehension and Analysis of Grade-Level-Appropriate Text	
2.2	Respond to *who, what, when, where,* and *how* questions.
2.3	Follow one-step written instructions.
2.4	Use context to resolve ambiguities about word and sentence meanings.
2.5	Confirm predictions about what will happen next in a text by identifying key words (i.e., signpost words).
2.6	Relate prior knowledge to textual information.
2.7	Retell the central ideas of simple expository or narrative passages.

3.0 **Literary Response and Analysis** Students read and respond to a wide variety of significant works of children's literature. They distinguish between the structural features of the text and the literary terms or elements (e.g., theme, plot, setting, characters). The selections in *Recommended Literature, Kindergarten Through Grade Twelve* illustrate the quality and complexity of the materials to be read by students.

Narrative Analysis of Grade-Level-Appropriate Text	
3.1	Identify and describe the elements of plot, setting, and character(s) in a story, as well as the story's beginning, middle, and ending.
3.2	Describe the roles of authors and illustrators and their contributions to print materials.
3.3	Recollect, talk, and write about books read during the school year.

WRITING

1.0 **Writing Strategies** Students write clear and coherent sentences and paragraphs that develop a central idea. Their writing shows they consider the audience and purpose. Students progress through the stages of the writing process (e.g., prewriting, drafting, revising, editing successive versions).

Organization and Focus

1.1 Select a focus when writing.

1.2 Use descriptive words when writing.

Penmanship

1.3 Print legibly and space letters, words, and sentences appropriately.

2.0 **Writing Applications (Genres and Their Characteristics)** Students write compositions that describe and explain familiar objects, events, and experiences. Student writing demonstrates a command of standard American English and the drafting, research, and organizational strategies outlined in Writing Standard 1.0.

Using the writing strategies of grade one outlined in Writing Standard 1.0, students:

2.1 Write brief narratives (e.g., fictional, autobiographical) describing an experience.

2.2 Write brief expository descriptions of a real object, person, place, or event, using sensory details.

WRITTEN AND ORAL ENGLISH LANGUAGE CONVENTIONS

The standards for written and oral English language conventions have been placed between those for writing and for listening and speaking because these conventions are essential to both sets of skills.

1.0 **Written and Oral English Language Conventions** Students write and speak with a command of standard English conventions appropriate to this grade level.

Sentence Structure

1.1 Write and speak in complete, coherent sentences.

Grammar

1.2 Identify and correctly use singular and plural nouns.

1.3 Identify and correctly use contractions (e.g., *isn't, aren't, can't, won't)* and singular possessive pronouns (e.g., *my/ mine, his/ her, hers, your/s)* in writing and speaking.

Punctuation

1.4 Distinguish between declarative, exclamatory, and interrogative sentences.

1.5 Use a period, exclamation point, or question mark at the end of sentences.

1.6 Use knowledge of the basic rules of punctuation and capitalization when writing.

Capitalization

1.7 Capitalize the first word of a sentence, names of people, and the pronoun *I*.

Spelling

1.8 Spell three-and four-letter short-vowel words and grade-level-appropriate sight words correctly.

LISTENING AND SPEAKING

1.0 **Listening and Speaking Strategies** Students listen critically and respond appropriately to oral communication. They speak in a manner that guides the listener to understand important ideas by using proper phrasing, pitch, and modulation.

Comprehension

1.1 Listen attentively.

1.2 Ask questions for clarification and understanding.

1.3 Give, restate, and follow simple two-step directions.

Organization and Delivery of Oral Communication

1.4 Stay on the topic when speaking.

1.5 Use descriptive words when speaking about people, places, things, and events.

2.0 **Speaking Applications (Genres and Their Characteristics)** Students deliver brief recitations and oral presentations about familiar experiences or interests that are organized around a coherent thesis statement. Student speaking demonstrates a command of standard American English and the organizational and delivery strategies outlined in Listening and Speaking Standard 1.0.

Using the speaking strategies of grade one outlined in Listening and Speaking Standard 1.0, students:

2.1 Recite poems, rhymes, songs, and stories.

2.2 Retell stories using basic story grammar and relating the sequence of story events by answering *who, what, when, where, why,* and *how* questions.

2.3 Relate an important life event or personal experience in a simple sequence.

2.4 Provide descriptions with careful attention to sensory detail.